LYDA N. ROCHMIS (M.A., Radcliffe College) has been a teacher of speech in New York City high schools for over thirty years and is currently acting chairman of the Speech Department of James Monroe High School. She has been president of the New York City Speech Association and editor of its *Bulletin,* and has contributed articles on speech to various educational journals.

DOROTHY DOOB (Ed.D., New York University) is Associate Professor of Speech at Hunter College of the City University of New York. She has many years of experience in supervising the training of prospective speech clinicians for the New York City school system and for hospital clinics. She holds the Certificate of Clinical Competence in Speech Pathology of the American Speech and Hearing Association. Professor Doob has presented papers at national and international conventions, including the 1968 conference of the International Society for the Rehabilitation of the Disabled at Hong Kong.

Speech Therapy

A Group Approach for Schools and Clinics

DATE DUE

AP 08 '97			
AP 22 '97			
AP 14 '97			

Speech

Lyda N. Rochmis
and
Dorothy Doob

Therapy

A Group Approach
for
Schools and Clinics

The John Day Company
New York

The John Day Company, Inc., 257 Park Avenue South, New York, N.Y. 10010.
Distributed in Elementary and High School by Steck-Vaughn Company, P.O.
Box 2028, Austin, Texas 78767

Intext companies

Published on the same day in Canada by Longmans Canada Limited.

Library of Congress Catalogue Card Number: 73-89310
Printed in the United States of America
Designed by The Etheredges

Contents

———◆———

v

CONTENTS

CONTENTS

Foreword

———◆———

Administrators and teachers of speech concerned with using the limited time of the speech clinic to the greatest advantage will find a methodology and momentum in this excellent text. Speech teachers in city schools usually deal with students in remedial classes or clinical groups. Conducting meaningful speech therapy in groups is a subject that has been neglected by textbooks, and supervisors have noted this deficiency when working with prospective teachers.

Varied and specific drill materials provided in this text are especially suitable for motivating the high school student and easily adaptable to other levels. There is a dearth of such material available to the busy teacher.

The authors' combined experience represents years of teaching and supervising of prospective teachers of speech in the training program at Hunter College of the City University of New York, and direct class and clinical teaching and supervision in a large urban high school. All professionals in the field will find many valuable suggestions for organizing and maintaining productive clinic programs. The arrangement of chapters along lines of actual organization of school clinics is very helpful.

The material presented here, tested through expert use, is best suited for the senior high school age range, but speech teachers of grades five through twelve, as well as speech therapists in college clinics, will find this book an excellent resource in planning for their students.

HELEN M. DONOVAN
Director, Bureau for
Speech Improvement
Board of Education, New York City

Preface

———◆———

It is our belief that the speech clinics of our elementary and secondary schools are underachievers. Although these clinics have come a long way, they have not tapped their full potential. There are in the field dedicated and knowledgeable therapists; there is growing public awareness and support; and there is a history of long and excellent progress in research and methodology, in some of which we ourselves have been privileged to participate. What our clinics now need are evaluative objectives to bridge the gap between rich theoretical backgrounds and the dynamics to make the theories workable and productive in a group therapy situation. We hope that this book will serve as a catalyst for the teaching materials avalanching down upon our present and prospective teachers of speech.

The purpose of the book is to help speech clinicians plan better and more efficient clinics. Our approach to the problem is twofold: We describe the goals to be achieved for the disorders handled in clinics and then present procedures for achieving them. Original drill material of a provocative type is included. In this way, our book will provide direction for newcomers to the field and a practicum for those who wish to evaluate what they are doing.

In the public schools, speech therapy is therapy in groups. That is what public funds provide; that is what teachers and supervisors must implement. In hospitals and private clinics, therapy is handled on an individual basis. While a one-to-one relationship in therapy has much to recommend it, we in public education must accept the fact that it is not generally feasible for us. Certain monies are available for the handicapped, including the speech handicapped, which enable schools to provide smaller sections for speech clinics. The speech teacher in a large school, however, must be prepared to achieve results in groups ranging from an ideal of eight to a pragmatic twenty.

The dynamics of group therapy differ materially from those of individual therapy. The number of students under group instruction, as well as those who would receive it if there were enough qualified personnel, is many times greater than the number receiving individual instruction. We know of no adequate guide that sets practical goals of achievement for students preparing to teach speech in the public schools, for those in college with the responsibility for training them, or for those already engaged in teaching. The prime concern of young professionals in the field of speech is not "What shall I teach?" but "When have I achieved a reasonable goal?" They want to know how much of the theory of speech is pertinent in the clinic, how to approach the problems of correction, when to branch off into supplementary material, and what to accept as nodes of achievement at different levels of progress. It is the purpose of this book to provide some of the answers to those questions. We assume that those to whom we direct it are already familiar with much of the subject matter and are concerned with finding a way to use the limited time of the clinic to the greatest advantage.

To this end, we believe that students in clinics must learn exactly what their problems are and what they might reasonably expect to achieve. They must be taught not only techniques of control but also how to drill and how to compose their own drills. A lisper, for instance, should not spend the term (and some have spent years!) learning how to make the sibilant. If he does not have a usable sound within the first two weeks, the clinic has not maintained a proper dynamic of achievement. When the student is fully aware of his problem and when he has participated in setting his own goal, then the many aspects of speech improvement have validity for him.

Furthermore, our book will introduce the prospective teacher to methods he can use in his own clinic. It will help the practicing teacher evaluate his own techniques. Many new types of drills are provided, as well as suggestions for composing them. For the beginning teacher, there is a rationale for a standard of speech and voice. Approaches to and procedures for the correction of common speech defects are described. Directions for referrals and sources of supplementary material are given. Included also are student self-help and self-evaluation forms. Where theory is presented, it is given to refresh the teacher's thinking. Teachers and teachers-to-be will find philosophy to guide them until such time as their own experience provides them with an individual point of view.

We are grateful to the New York City school system, which has permitted much individual experimentation and contributed to the growth of an individual point of view. Our sincere gratitude is extended to our good friends and colleagues whose encouragement in the early stages of authorship helped us create a book out of a manuscript. In particular we thank Dr. Helen Donovan, Dr. Letitia Raubicheck, Dr. Francis Griffith, Professor Marvin Seiger, Professor Jennie Calahan, and Professor F. Fulton Ross.

For their time, patience, and perspicacity in proofreading the manuscript, Dr. Arthur Nathan, Professor Mary Sheehan, and Martha Kraus deserve and receive from us a lasting indebtedness.

We are indebted also to the staff of the James Monroe High School library and especially to Eleanor Berliner and Emma Stolz. Their tracking ability was second to none.

For his wholehearted identification with the writing as it progressed and his carefully executed diagrams, we express our deep appreciation to the late Joseph La Scala.

For her personal concern and professional competency in photography, we are grateful to Marlis Schwieger.

Where the writing abutted on the demands of daily living and where pressures threatened decision's judicial poise, it was Louis L. Baumritter, husband of Professor Doob, who, with his tact and counsel, brought us needed respite and a sense of achievement.

To the editorial staff of The John Day Company, and especially to Elizabeth Swift, we express our appreciation and gratitude for their patience and professional concern.

L. N. R.
D. D.

Speech Therapy

A Group Approach for Schools and Clinics

I

The Opening Lessons

———◆———

HOW TO OBTAIN A WORKABLE GROUP

You are a beginning teacher of speech in a large public school. You have a typical program consisting of, perhaps, four speech clinics and an English class, or three clinics and two English classes. For the classes in English the course of study is set: You have graded and required texts, spelling, etymology, composition, literature, and supplementary reading. What is the course of study for the speech clinics? Are the requirements equally definite? Are the procedures specified? What is basically required for the first week of teaching? What is considered a term's accomplishment?

You hasten to answer that the clinic is not a textbook class, that you work with individuals on individual problems. Your head, moreover, is crammed with the theories you have studied; you are aware that the library is bulging with information on the subject of speech disorders and techniques of speech therapy;

and you have spent many hours as a practice or practicing teacher. The teaching situation you envisage is rarely the one you meet in the schools. There the reality of the speech teacher's program is that a clinic meets X times a week, that it may comprise a wholesome maximum of eight students or an unwholesome aggregate of thirty; that it may be homogeneously workable or nonhomogeneously disparate.

Whatever the situation, you, the teacher, are responsible for providing educationally sound therapy for the students looking for help with their speech problems. This chapter aims to provide an orientation to the actual teaching situation.

Your first job, which is completely different from that of an ordinary classroom teacher, is to find out whether or not the students have previously attended a speech clinic, the exact nature of their problems, and what they expect of the clinic. The school undoubtedly subscribes to the principle of the homogeneous speech clinic — but probably not the practice. It is often difficult to achieve this goal because of the large number of students needing help and the limited number of teachers available. In a large school system, the speech classes are likely to be the stepchildren of the schedule, so that it falls to you, the speech teacher, to see to it that the clinic is one that can function, and that you have a workable group.

Defining a Workable Group

What is meant by a workable group? Let us consider two of your classes, class A and class B. Each has a registration of twenty students. This is somewhat large but still an acceptable class size, although fifteen is usually considered ideal in a large city system. Are both classes equally workable? You set about to find out: by listening to each student speak and read; by consulting the notations of the recommending teacher; by checking the speech file and if necessary administering a diagnostic speech test. Some teachers prefer to consult the speech file first and reconcile it with their own evaluation; others, generally the more experienced teachers, prefer to make their own diagnosis first.

The problem, however, is not yours alone. Each student under your care must recognize his own problem so that even while you may be acutely aware of the nature of the speech defect or disorder, you must seek to involve the student in the problem immediately. Ask him what he considers his problem to be and whether he has worked in a speech class before. If additional information is needed, have the student read either an ordinary selection at his grade level, or a specially weighted one. Make a notation of your observations on the record, and be sure that the student knows the name and nature of his problem. Arrange a personal conference with each student who seems unwilling to recognize his speech problem or to be assigned to a speech clinic. Your initial class meeting is not the time to help these negative, protesting students.

Now to return to the evaluation of your two classes. Class A, you discover, has four lallers, two students with markedly substandard diction, and the rest run the gamut of lisping. This is a workable group. The drills required are similar. It can work as a single unit functioning five or fewer times a week. Individualization of the work involving specially planned drills for each group must, understandably, be part of all speech practice. Here individualization has a peripheral value for each of the groups within the class.

Class B also has twenty students, but it is not a workable group. Three are stutterers, two have marked nasality, two have husky voices, and the rest are lispers. Stutterers obviously require a special climate and a different approach from that for students with voice and articulation problems. The cases of nasality may be entirely dissimilar, one representing cleft palate speech, another hypertension, and a third, assimilated nasality. Class B must be rescheduled.

It is hoped that the teacher will have the confidence and support of the administration to the extent that he can reallocate the periods within the schedule that have been assigned to him. More can be accomplished for each group by programming students with similar defects to meet by themselves once or twice a week. Better results can be expected in a shorter time with a homogeneous group than can be achieved with a nonhomogeneous group meeting for a full week. The loss of clinic time to a child who, having been scheduled for five periods, now has only two, can be compensated for further by turning over the responsibility of drill to him and by the use of daily practice schemes — e.g., diaries and reports. A suggested scheduling of the nonhomogeneous B class is this:

STUTTERERS: *twice a week*
LISPERS: *twice a week*
VOICE GROUP: *once a week*

Your first job is done; your responsibility has been met. Your classes have been divided into workable groups!

THE SPEECH PROFILE

The speech clinic is now homogeneously organized and you are ready to begin a program of therapy. Your next responsibility is to learn as much as you can of the physical and physiological background of each of your students. The child who comes for speech help is a physical entity. That child must be evaluated before any speech therapy you administer is valid. The teacher, generally, is neither physician nor psychologist but he does have special training and the sensitive and discerning ear needed to verify these essentials:

1. Is there a tongue-tie?

PROCEDURE: The teacher checks the movement of the tongue by asking the student to lift the tongue — first with the mouth half open and then in a wide-open position. If the student can do this easily, there is no problem of

4

tongue-tie. If, however, the teacher observes that the frenum is attached too far forward, impeding the movement of the tongue, a diagnosis of suspected tongue-tie may be made. In this case, it would be the teacher's responsibility to refer the student to the school doctor or nurse for further verification of the diagnosis. If the diagnosis of tongue-tie is substantiated, the student will be referred to the proper agency for the clipping of the frenum. The child should be informed that this is a minor procedure generally less unpleasant than the pulling of a tooth. It must be remembered, however, that the responsibility of the decision rests with the parent.

2. Is the tongue working to capacity? Can it point? Can it touch a small specific area?

PROCEDURE: The teacher demonstrates the accurate functioning of the tongue by placing the tip on the midpoint of the upper lip. Then he touches each corner of the mouth, points the tip up, and then down. The students, using mirrors, do the same, observing themselves and evaluating their accuracy in tongue placement.

3. What are the general characteristics of the tongue? Is it large and fleshy? Are there ridges? Is it proportionately shaped? Is it overlong, foreshortened?

PROCEDURE: As the students observe each of these aspects, noting their observations on the forms in front of them, the teacher also watches and comments. He will probably be called upon to help the students form their judgments, since this is an area in which they have had little basis for comparison.

4. Does the bite approximate? Is there malocclusion? Do the teeth come together at the sides? Is there a marked overbite (buckteeth) or any overbite at all? Is the jaw undershot? Is there an open bite?

PROCEDURE: The teacher instructs the students to assume a bite position, bringing their side teeth together normally, as in chewing. He must make sure that they do not attempt to force the teeth to meet in the front. The teacher directs the students to note and sense this position. The normal bite position is essential in correcting several articulatory defects and will be used as a basis in future exercises. Some students may already be receiving orthodontic treatment or wearing braces, a fact the teacher should note. He may recommend to others that their parents consider such treatment for them.

5. Are the teeth regular? Do they slant in? (If so, the tongue loses valuable space for functioning.) Do they slant out? Are there irregularities? Are there extra teeth, missing teeth, overlapping teeth, chipped teeth, spaces?

PROCEDURES: The teacher first finds out from the students what dental work is in progress. Dental conditions are clearly the province of the dentist or orthodontist. The students then note on their profile forms any problems in this area with which they have to cope. (Since teeth cannot be capped until fully developed, generally not before eighteen years of age, younger children will have to live for a while with the problem of a chipped tooth.)

6. Is the palatal arch rounded? Is it narrow or high? Is it both high and narrow?

PROCEDURES: This is an area where experience is needed and only the teacher's judgment is valid. His observations should be added to the speech profile.

7. Is there a hearing loss?

PROCEDURES: Only an audiometric test should be relied on. The teacher, however, may want to make a preliminary judgment. If he suspects a hearing loss, he may consult the student's health record to see if a test has been given.

If there is no such record, it would be his responsibility to refer the student to the school doctor or nurse for an audiometric evaluation.

It is understandable that, at the beginning of the semester, the teacher is torn between finding out in the shortest time possible just what the physical background of each pupil is, as represented by the questions above, and the necessity of getting the class organized and the therapy started. These two objectives are not, however, irreconcilable if the teacher uses a system of cooperative exploration.

Cooperative Exploration

Each child is provided with a guide sheet (see form at the end of the chapter) and an unbreakable mirror — hopefully supplied by the school. Under careful teacher direction and demonstration, the student observes himself, often cooperating with his neighbor to arrive at a judgment. When in doubt he may consult the teacher. To the best of his ability he answers each question on the profile sheet. After each category the teacher checks the answers, corroborating the student's judgment or amending it. In practice this has many advantages: it saves valuable class time at the beginning of the term; it familiarizes the student with his own physical equipment for speech, and serves to interest him in his own problems. The student, for instance, who discovers his own tongue-tie — a condition not unknown, unfortunately, even among students of high school age — needs no further motivation. The student who asks, "Will the slant of my teeth prevent me from making a good /s/ sound?" and is assured that it will not, but that he will have to correct the placement of the tip of his tongue, has already applied his intelligence to the problem.

When these profiles have been studied by the teacher, rechecked individually with the students where necessary, the comments should be transcribed to the speech record card. A second step in a very satisfactory beginning has been made.

SPEECH PROFILE: STUDENT SELF-EXAMINATION FORM

The following questions are to be answered by the student under the direction of the teacher. Listen for the explanation of each item and answer it to the best of your ability. Have your mirror available. A "yes" or "no" answer to each question is required. Consult the teacher if in doubt.

TONGUE

Does it point? _____

Does it touch the gum ridge when the mouth is half open? _____ wide open? _____

Can it maintain accuracy? _____ (Touch the tongue-tip to the upper lip at the midpoint and at either side.)

Describe the tongue. (Check one) Quite long _____ Flabby _____ Ridged _____ Split or indented at front _____ Normal _____

TEETH

Are there any irregularities? Uneven _____ where? _____ Extra _____ where? _____ Chipped _____ where? _____ Missing? _____ where? _____

Are there any spaces? _____ where? _____

Braces? _____ When put on? _____ When coming off? _____

Do they slant in? _____ Slant out? _____ Are they "buck" teeth? _____

OCCLUSION

Is there an overbite? _____

Is the jaw undershot? _____

Is there an open bite? _____

Hold a normal bite position for a moment or two. Are you certain of it? _____

PALATAL ARCH

Is it rounded? _____ Narrow? _____ Vaulted? _____

ANSWER THE FOLLOWING QUESTIONS:

Have you a hearing difficulty? _____ Do you suspect a hearing loss? _____ Would you like a hearing test? _____ Have you a cold now? _____ Do you get colds frequently? _____ Have you a sinus condition? _____ Asthma? _____ Hay fever? _____ Allergies? _____

II

Who Has a Speech Defect?
Setting and Selling
a Standard of Speech

————◆————

Perhaps we should pause at this point in our pursuit of a solidly functioning speech clinic to consider a peripheral but vital aspect of our work; namely, who has a speech defect, and which defects are considered most serious? Speech defects vary from minor articulatory problems to more serious disorders such as stuttering. In addition, a defect may be more of a social stigma to one person than to another. Several elements must be taken into consideration in evaluating the need for therapy. A problem often faced in large schools is that of selecting the students who can be accommodated and assigned to clinics. (Teachers and classes available are both limited.) In a school of 4,000, for instance, using the generally accepted percentage of incidence — 4 percent — the school survey should indicate about 160 students in need of speech therapy. This number does not, of course, include the non-English-speaking students. The school, however, has classroom space for only 100 and must postpone scheduling 60 for a future term. Who should be selected? Which are the more serious speech deviations that should be treated first?

This question was once answered with deep insight by Dr. Letitia Raubicheck, nationally known speech authority, who said in a class for prospective teachers of speech, "That defect which is socially or economically stigmatizing to a person is the most serious one." Thus, a college applicant, a would-be actor, secretary, salesman, lawyer, politician, or disadvantaged person might be in greater need of immediate speech therapy for a lesser defect than a young person whose substandard diction, though grossly offensive by cultural standards, was of no concern to him. One aspect of the speech teacher's job is, of course, to arouse that concern, but this may be a long and involved process. The needs of students with lesser defects and greater economic and social demands should not always be sacrificed to those with gross substandard speech.

There is a second generalization that should guide us in selecting students for the speech clinic. Speech does not exist in a vacuum — physical or social. It is *always* communication; it is *always* a composite. In some patterns of speech, certain defects preclude communication, in others they do not. This has great significance for the speech clinic, then, because our object is *never* merely the elimination of a lisp, the eradication of a faulty /l/ or /r/ sound. It is always the general improvement of the speech pattern, focusing on the specific problem involved. This is not semantic hair-splitting, but the core of an attitude that involves both the teacher and the student. It is the basic tenet of the speech improvement class.

A speech teacher is often asked about people in public life, including the President of the United States or a Senator, "Has he good speech? Hasn't he a lisp? Isn't his voice nasal? Doesn't he mispronounce his /s/ [/sh/, /r/ or /l/] sound?" In most cases the answer is something like this: "Yes, he has a lisp — or a lall — BUT he is an excellent speaker. Don't you find it interesting to listen to him? Isn't he clear? His rate of speaking, firm use of emphasis, effective pauses, voice projection are all excellent. Of course, it *would* be better if he did not have the lisp, but you must consider the entire speech and communication pattern before making a judgment."

Furthermore, it is a truism of speech work that the student's own interest in self-improvement wins half the battle. An amusing story illustrates this point: A bright boy with unwarrantedly slovenly speech suddenly evinced a great desire to be assigned to a speech clinic. "The sooner, the better," he said. His teacher was delighted and secretly exultant — but woe to pedagogical pride and hurrah for primary motivation! He had just been smitten with a girl attending a special school for drama and the performing arts! He needed speech improvement in a hurry.

The problem of time and space is always with us. We have given thought to the question of who should be in the speech clinic. We must also be ready to apportion its *time* to obtain the greatest good for the greatest number. In this connection, the clinician must recognize improvement and be willing to accept results that can be reconciled with a reasonable prognosis. It may be better for a student to be discharged after making reasonable progress. The teacher should be willing to accept improvement in a variety of speech skills as well as in the student's major problem. These skills may include improvement in phrasing, in using more meaningful voice modulation, and improvement in the student's audience relationship. The clinician must determine the stage at which the student can be expected to go on by himself. In this, a mutual challenge, the student can and should be taken into a partnership. He should be made to understand what the teacher has in mind for him and not taken on a vague voyage to an impossible harbor of achievement. There should be a reasonable goal with intermediate points of success. Let him admire the diction of Richard Burton and Geraldine Page and the clean, clear reading of e. e. cummings. In fact, make appreciation of diction and interpretation a part of what you teach, but set his goal on a path that the student can recognize and follow. That he will find and achieve more than he realizes is the clinician's secret weapon.

The average student has rarely considered, consciously, what constitutes "good" or "substandard" speech until his presence in a corrective class or clinic brings that question to the fore. It is a healthy and important thing for him to consider. Much of your success as a clinician hinges on his involvement in what he is doing. Here is a fine opportunity for you to capture his imagination! The questions that follow serve to stimulate meaningful discussion.

- What is dialect? Do we have different dialects in the United States?
- Is there more than one acceptable standard of speech?
- Who is responsible for setting these standards, and how do they do it?
- Should an individual use a different type of speech in different situations? Is it democratic to do so?
- How are standards set in other countries — *i.e.,* France?
- Why are dictionaries authoritative? Are they equally so?
- What is meant by "preferred" pronunciations in the dictionary? Should we prefer them?
- What is phonetics? How wide a divergence is there between spelling and pronunciation? Why?
- Should there be a different speech standard for blacks and whites?
- Do the British speak better than Americans?
- What standard should I set for myself?

The answers to these and many similar questions can be found in books such as: *The Pronunciation of American English* (Bronstein), *American Pronunciation* (Kenyon), *Pronunciation of Standard English in America* (Krapp), *Sounds of Spoken English* (Ripman), and other sources listed in the Selected Bibliography.

12

WHO HAS A SPEECH DEFECT?

The teacher or clinician who launches a group with a barrage of questions such as the above and sifts from the students' answers the elements of prejudice, ignorance, and confusion as to what constitutes standard speech will have a lead as to where to begin the work of the class. He will be able to give direction to the curiosity and interest of the class — a first step toward self-improvement. It is the hope of every speech group to arrive at a definition of standard speech that is acceptable to the students, to inculcate an attitude toward speech excellence, and to develop a rationale for setting a personal standard. It is an objective that must be realized early in the term. Improvement in communicative clarity, toward which all the work of the speech clinic is directed, depends in great part on the motivation and perseverance of the students involved.

By definition [1] "good diction is that used by the majority of educated people in a region." Anyone who has ever tried to frame such a definition knows that it must be couched in just such broad terms — terms that are, however, meaningless unless one has had a broad spectrum of professional, day-to-day experience to substantiate them. Our students have not. In fact, the "experts" are not always in accord. In 1950,[2] a survey was made of standards of speech required in oral tests for teaching throughout the country. The results of this survey shocked many people in the speech field. *More than 50 percent* of the appointing officers, for example, were willing to accept the pronunciation "idear of." [3] Some accepted a metathesized "childern." Another 50 percent, on the other hand, would not permit the short form "John 'n' Mary," although it is generally considered not only

[1] Francis Griffith, Catherine Nelson, and Edward Stasheff, *Your Speech* (New York, Harcourt, Brace & World, 1960), p. 173.
[2] Arthur J. Bronstein and Mardel Ogilvie, "A Report on Methods, Content and Speech Standards of the Oral Interview Used in Teachers' Qualifying Examinations," *Speech Bulletin* of the New York City Speech Association (March, 1951).
[3] Ten years later a U.S. President made the pronunciation familiar, if not acceptable.

13

acceptable but the preferred pronunciation. Yet another 50 percent insisted on "natyure" as against "nacher," although Jones [4] long ago accepted the latter (neɪtʃə). Fairbanks [5] goes as far as to say:

> Acceptability of pronunciation is determined exclusively by usage in the population. No pronunciation is acceptable or unacceptable *a priori;* no word is restricted to one acceptable pronunciation; every acceptable pronunciation or set of pronunciations of any word is subject to change. Good general dictionaries record some but not all of the acceptable pronunciations. If a given pronunciation does not appear, you may not conclude that it is unacceptable.

DEVELOPING A RATIONALE

We do, however, identify substandard speech and we must help our students to do likewise, particularly if they have been sent to us with so-called substandard speech. As a first step, let them question their own thinking about the standards they apply. Here is one tested procedure for doing so:

Place on the board a commonly used and commonly mispronounced word such as "asked." Caution the students not to make judgments of right or wrong, but to volunteer all pronunciations of the word they may ever have heard. A list such as the following will appear:

1. ɑskt	6. est
2. ɛ́əskt	7. ɛ̃st
3. askè d	8. ækst
4. eskt	9. æskt
5. æst	10. askt

[4] Daniel Jones, *An English Pronouncing Dictionary* (New York, Dutton, 1964), p. 320.
[5] Grant Fairbanks, *Voice and Articulation Drillbook,* 2d ed., 1960, p. 104. Reprinted by permission of Harper & Row, Publishers.

Now ask the students to rule out just *one* of these pronunciations for their own use, giving as specific a reason as possible for doing so. Reject such answers as "It doesn't sound right" or "Only a Brooklynite [or a Bronxite] would say it" or "I don't like it." With some probing, you will end with a set of criteria like these:

1. Britishism — out of place here
2. vulgarism — used in "type" acting
3. misinterpretation of the spelling — except in some poetry
4. foreignism — particularly Yiddish
5. omission — no justification for it.
6. combination of 4 and 5
7. both vulgarism and omission
8. infantilism, metathesis
9. General American — acceptable
10. acceptable, especially for actors

We now can formulate a definition for the use of students, which they should write in their notebooks for future reference:

> In setting a standard of speech for ourselves, we should eliminate pronunciations which are characterized by foreignisms, omissions or additions, vulgarisms, Britishisms, infantilisms, ignorance (misinterpretation) of spelling, or accentuation.

We see by this analysis that it is the individual's right and obligation to exclude pronunciations which logic indicates to him are incorrect. An analysis such as the above will spur him on to become better informed.

It is certainly not required that we involve students in the minutiae of speech standards, but it is absolutely necessary for the student to think about the problem and to relate his thinking to his own speech. And when our students will have learned to judge for themselves, they will be equally aware that other people are judging them. They will be willing to acknowledge the right of the school to set minimal standards of good speech and to encourage maximal ambition, not excluding that of sheer snobbery.

ACCENTUATION IN WORDS

Another concept that is useful for the student to understand at the outset is the tendency in a highly accented language like English (or Russian) to pronounce fully only one syllable in a word, and to weaken the others. This causes a change in the quantity of the vowel sound in accordance with its position in the word. In an unstressed position, the vowel is weak, light, colorless. The most common weak sound in English, and in other languages, is known as the *schwa*, a term meaning "weak" used in the International Phonetic Alphabet and written like an *e* upside down — namely, ə. Observe the pronunciation of the five written vowels in tonic (accented), pre- and post-tonic positions:

Tonic		*Pre-tonic*	*Post-tonic*
A	matter, made	about	adamant, literature
E	imbedded, breeze	enough	loaded, lamentable
I	biting, embittered	immense	authoritative
O	phone, monotonous	olympic, hotel	monotone, monotonous
U	bunting, illuminate	umbrella, summation	usual, unctuous

There are other weak sounds: a weak form of the short /ɪ/ written in narrow transcription /ɪᵻ t/ and a weak form of /oʊ/, actually the first part of the diphthong /o/. These are not as common as the schwa.

It is interesting to observe how widespread a tendency of language it is to weaken sounds. Even two languages as disparate as English and Russian demonstrate this tendency. Here is a sentence in Russian, transliterated by means of common phonetic symbols plus the sign (') after a consonant when it is palatalized or pronounced soft. Read in this way, it would be completely understandable to a Russian:

16

prəf'e'sə * skəzal' ʃtə nam' nu'ʒnə gəvarit" i dumət' pə ru'skɪ

Now, the same sentence in English, "The professor said that we must speak and think in Russian" would look like this in phonetics:

ðə prəfe'sə sed' ðət wi məst spik' ən θɪŋk' ɪn rʌ'ʃn

Can we fail to see the tendency of both languages to use the schwa in unaccented words and syllables? In a class whose purpose it is to improve communicative clarity, not only the pronunciation of a sound or sounds, we can see the importance of this principle.

The students have probably already observed or been taught that stress is associated with meaning. It may be well to reemphasize the fact that grammatical variants and differences in meaning are produced by changing the stress pattern of a word. Some common examples are:

pro' duce	(n)	pro duce'	(v)
con' duct	(n)	con duct'	(v)
per' fume	(n)	per fume'	(v)
es' cort	(n)	es cort'	(v)
rec' ord	(n)	re cord'	(v)
ab' sent	(adj)	ab sent'	(v)
reb' el	(n)	re bel'	(v)

WEAK AND STRONG WORDS

Not only syllables, however, but strictly functional words such as prepositions, articles, conjunctions, personal pronouns, and auxiliary verbs are weakened when the weight of sense is not

* In phonetics, the stress mark precedes the syllable stressed. We have chosen to use the system in general dictionaries, where the stress mark follows the syllable stressed, so as not to confuse the students.

17

upon them in the phrase or sentence. This is called their weak form, as opposed to strong form, and is the one that is most often used. Note the difference in meaning between the following pairs of sentences:

Have you heard' about Mary?	(There is some news.)
Have you' heard about Mary?	(Well, so you know, too.)
Please hand' me a pen'.	(I need a small favor.)
Please hand me a' pen.	(I didn't ask for the entire box!)
Is this' his home'?	(Have we reached there?)
Is this his' home?	(There's something unusual about it — I'm amazed.)
Florence' and Ruth' are coming'.	(We can expect them.)
Florence and' Ruth are coming.	(You'll have to make provision for both.)
He's speaking' with me' about it.	(We're having a consultation.)
He's speaking with' me about it.	(He's on my side, not on the other.)

Students at both elementary and high school levels are often completely ignorant of the existence of weak sounds and weak forms and, until guided to do so, are unwilling to accept them as a proper standard in conversational speech. They may have been conditioned by a type of wooden recitation favored in the lower grades and consider normal conversational standards too informal. A teacher may have to strive vigorously against this point of view.

SYLLABIFICATION

Syllabification is intimately connected with pronunciation. Students who generally have no trouble in pronouncing the syllables of a word often ask what rules there are to guide them in

18

this matter. Syllabification for speaking and writing differs in some words and is the same in others. A word has as many syllables as it has vowel sounds, except when the three syllabic consonants, *l, m* and *n* take the place of the vowel:

re mar ka ble (note silent final *e*)   rəmar′kəbl
si lent   saɪ′lənt
si lence   saɪ′ləns
lit tle   lɪ′*tl*
cha sm   kæ′zm
hea ven   he′vn

In speaking, all consonants that are normally pronounced together — that is, that exist as blends at the beginning of words — may also be pronounced together at the beginning of syllables. Impossible combinations — that is, those that cannot be pronounced together — are separated. The phonetic transcription of course reflects this:

im pos si ble   ɪm pɒ′sɪ bl
un ten a ble   ʌn ten′ə bl
wil ful   wɪl′fəl
sym pa thy   sɪm′pə θɪ
luck less   lʌk′ləs

BUT [pronounceable blends]

re sti tu tion   re stɪ tju′ʃn
es tab lish   e stæ′blɪʃ
stra to sphere   stræ′to sfɪɚ

In writing, it is also true that there are as many syllables as there are vowel sounds, that the syllabic consonants may take the place of a vowel, and that impossible consonant combinations are separated. The differences are these: Two identical consonants are always separated even though they represent only one sound:

slam ming   lit tle (but sipped is sipt)

A consonant that would normally be pronounced at the beginning of a syllable is often written with the preceding one to indicate that its vowel is short. Thus,

cat a pult	but	ma jor
mod ern	but	ro ta ry
nod ule	but	no tor i ous

In addition, written syllabification attempts to maintain etymological purity by separating prefixes and suffixes from stems:

pre fix, re fer   (but, pref ace, ref er ence)
pack ing, strong er   (but, dis tin guish, sin gly)

In other words, we have no conflicting rules in oral syllabification, whereas those for written language do conflict.

THE R IN TRANSITION

Another general tendency of language for students to understand is that not only language itself changes, but that individual sounds change over the years. An excellent example of this is found in the fairly recent changes of the sound of r. There are many /r/ sounds heard and studied by our students — the trilled r of Italian, the so-called uvular r of French (recently shown by slow X-ray film not to employ the uvula at all), the English single-tap r, and the German guttural. In American English we distinguish, first, between the consonant r and the inverted vowel pronunciation of General American speech, and then between this latter pronunciation and a variant standard which drops the /r/ sound entirely.

20

The reason for all this variation is, of course, that the /r/ sound has been in transition since the twelfth century. From its Germanic (Anglo-Saxon) origin through a lighter, trilled period of pronunciation (Middle English), it has undergone, and is still undergoing, a streamlining process. In the sentence "We are rarely free from fear," only three of the six *r*'s would be pronounced by *all Americans* — those in *free, from,* and the first *r* in *rarely.* The others become vocalic in different ways: In *are* we may pronounce an inverted /ɑ˞/ or drop the /r/ sound altogether /ɑ/; in *rarely* the second *r* is represented by the schwa in the new diphthong /ɛɚ/pronounced, we note again, with inversion in General American, or not /ɛə/; in *fear* it is represented by the schwa in the new diphthong /ɪɚ/.

In the course of the streamlining process, the *r* has been responsible for a new sound in the language; namely, the *er* or *ur,* pronounced /ɝ/ or /ɜ/. Words like *third, heard,* and *pert* were once pronounced as spelled. Try them that way with a wee trill and see if you don't feel that you come from a distant country or a rural section where dialects are still preserved. Today in cosmopolitan speech these spellings have all been streamlined into one sound, pronounced with or without inversion. When you discuss the /r/ sound with your students, let them know a little of what has been happening and why. It will spare you a great number of questions about spelling and will help your students acquire that knowledge of pronunciation that is authority.

It has been said that if George Washington returned to the capital he would not understand much of what was being said on the floor of Congress. The pundit will perceive the truth of the statement in financial terms, the linguist in semantic ones. We may be sure it is also true of pronunciation. Since it is part of our job in the speech clinic to equip the student to evaluate speech — both his own and that of others — lessons on language tendencies point out to him the distinction between true language — *i.e.,* what is spoken — and the written language. George Bernard Shaw could not change that dichotomy either by his personal dedication or by a generous monetary grant. Written English represents a long history — of Romans trying to spell Anglo-Saxon with Latin letters, thereby losing for us our thorn ð; of the Norman conquest, which left us a backwash of French words, some of which we anglicized and some of which we didn't — *banquet* /bæŋ'kwit/ but *ballet* /bæleɪ'/.

It would be an interesting and valuable experiment at the close of a unit on standards in speech to again ask the questions at the beginning of this chapter. In this way we can see how much more understanding of language the students have achieved and can evaluate their grasp of principles.

III
Techniques of the Drill

———◆———

THE BASIC DRILL

Most drills are valuable for most students, although some are more specifically pointed in the direction of their own problems. Unless students understand this, it will be awkward to ask them to participate, as they must and should, in group work. Yet group work is efficacious, economical of time, and basically what public education requires of clinics. In group work a drill to start or to end a period is a recommended procedure. This should be a simple drill with the possibility of many variations, such as the following, which we call a "basic" drill:

> Use three front vowels (in order to place the articulation forward in the mouth) representing three levels of tongue position — high, mid, and low. "Attach" the sound to be drilled, first in front of the vowel, and then after it. To illustrate with the sound of *t* aspirate:

1. tē (ti)	4. ēt (it)
2. tā (teɪ)	5. āt (eɪt)
3. tī (taɪ)	6. īt (aɪt)

Now, double the utterance:

1. tē tē	4. ēt ēt
2. tā tā	5. āt āt
3. tī tī	6. īt īt

Triple the utterance, working for lightness and fluency:

1. tē tē tē	4. ēt ēt ēt
2. tā tā tā	5. āt āt āt
3. tī tī tī	6. īt īt īt

Almost every consonant sound or combination can be drilled in this manner. The use of hand signals is a short cut. The clinician announces, for example, "the basic drill on *sp,* holds up one finger of the left hand and leads the class with the right hand, changing to two fingers for the double utterance and three for the triple. A twist of the left hand can indicate the reverse order (see steps 4 through 6 in drills above). Not only will this mechanization save time but it will help place drill in proper perspective for the students. They are, you will discover, very fond of routines if they're not overdone.

THE CLINICIAN'S ROLE

The major contribution of the speech clinician in drills is to look and listen. It is quite possible to detect individual variations, to comment on them and to individualize the instruction for a few moments. Where the student has an articulation (or pronunciation) difficulty that shows up in the course of a drill, explain the correct articulation (pronunciation) to him so that he can both hear it and form it. Special material can then be assigned for practice at home and subsequently checked. This means record keeping, but it is of great value. The teacher may elect to work with the cumulative speech record card provided by most schools, or keep his own type of record.

It is valuable for the clinician to remember that the speech clinic is like a gymnasium in some respects. There are drills for general muscular tone, precision drills, drills for sound discrimination, ear-training drills, drills to recognize and build rhythm patterns. Students leaving the physical education class after a period of exercise feel that they have had a workout. In the same way, students leaving the speech clinic should also feel that they have had a workout. No clinician needs to be reminded that drilling is largely physical; many have to be informed that speech is not completely intellectual.

THE COMPARATIVE DRILL

A discriminatory, or comparative, drill is most useful in the speech clinic. In this type of drill, words approximately similar in every respect except the one element to be drilled, are placed in juxtaposition. The student, if he is to differentiate the words at all, must do so through the sounds under consideration. Since we tend to confuse sounds that are similar, these drills will stimulate accuracy in hearing, performance, and judgment. Most standard texts in voice and diction are excellent sources of such drill material. A drill of this type useful for students of Spanish background is the following, in which the student must learn and then make automatic the different lip positions for /f-v/ and /p-b/. The clinician may wish to shorten the drill given here. Since the /f-v/ position is the more difficult for Spanish-speaking (ESL) students, it is placed first in the paired words. Reversing the order, i.e., bee – fee is a follow-up form of the drill.

COMPARATIVE DRILL /f-v/ AND /p-b/

fee – bee, feat – peat, fief – beef, freeze – breeze, freed – breed, fiend – beaned, fever – beaver, flea – bleed, visa – Pisa, feats of –

pizza, fees – peas, feasible – peaceable, veal – Bea'll, fleas – please, feel – peel, feast – beast, fear – peer, veer – beer, freezing – precinct

fig – pig, fib – bib, fin – pin, filled – build, Phil – pill, filly – Billy, fickle – pickle, flicker – bicker, Frigidaire – bridge is there, fiscal – biscuit, fiddling – piddling, vivid – pivot, vitiate – propitiate, vixen – pixies, vigor – bigger, fitch – pitch, live on tea – liberty

fled – bled, fetter – better, felt – pelt, veldt – belt, pheasant – peasant, ferry – Perry, fell – pellmell, vend – bend, fellows – bellow, Flemish – blemish, vent – bent, very – berry, vest – best, fender – bender, fence – pence, defendant – dependent, fester – pester, Fred – bread, every – Eberly

flame – blame, face – base, flayed – blade, frail – Braille, faced – baste, vacate – bake cake, veil – bail, vain – pain, vapor – paper, faker – baker, fated – pated, favor – paver, fair – pair, vein – bane

fang – pang, flaxseed – black seed, flank – blank, flank it – blanket, have it – habit, vamp her – pamper, camp fire – vampire, van – pan, vat – bat, fashion – passion, fatter – patter, fattened – patent, fast – past, fad – pad, fact – pact, fang – pang, fancy – pansy, vast – bass, fad – pad, fact – pact, flank – plank, fraternal – paternal, valet – palate

flight – plight, fried – bride, file – bile, via – bias, viable – Bible, vied – pied, fright – bright, fight – bite, virus – pirates, vise – pies, vile – bile, viper – piper, variety – pariah, fly – ply, friar – prior, fry – pry

fruit – brute, flew – blew, feel – peel, fume – plume, view – pew, voodoo – boo hoo, fewer – pure

foot – put, full – bull

fro – pro, phony – pony, foal – pole, volt – bolt, vote – boat, rove – robe, vocal – poker, volar – polar, Volga – polka, 'phone – bone, flow – blow ford – board, four – bore, fraught – brought, fraud – broad, vault – Baltic, Voss – boss, fawn – pawn, void – buoyed, voice – poise, foil – boil

folly –Polly, fodder – plodder, flock – block, forage – porridge, vomit – bomb it, fog – bog, fond – pond, fox – box, fossil – possible

far – par, farce – parse, farcial – partial, found – pound, flout – pout, vowel – bowel, vow – bow, frown – brown, foundry – boundary, fowl – Powell, flower – plower

fur – burr, furrow – borough, furl – pearl, flirt – blurt, verb – blurb, fern – burn, verse – purse, furnace – Ber'nice, furnish – burnish, first – burst, firmament – permanent, first step – percept

flush – blush, fudge – budge, flood – blood, fluster – bluster, funnel – bundle, fun – bun, front – brunt, fussed – bust, fuss – bus, flutter – butter, fuzz – buzz, of it – orbit

It will readily be seen that the above drill has certain fringe benefits in that the words are arranged according to the vowel scale. Questions of meaning, spelling, and homonyms may sometimes have to be touched upon, but such discussion should be limited to maintaining interest and validity.

Vowels that are commonly confused are best drilled in this manner. Thus, a comparative drill for the /æ/ as in *cat* to be differentiated from the /ɛɚ/ as in *care* would be:

COMPARATIVE DRILL ă (æ) AND ɛ (ɛɚ)

add	air	fan	fare	rack	rare
actor	airy	family	fairy	Sally	Sarah
am	ere	vanity	vary	stack	stare
pan	pair	than	there	scan	scare
band	bare	Nan	ne'er	sham	share
man	mare	tarry	tear (v)	chat	chair
wham	where	dad	dare	cat	care

27

COMPARATIVE DRILL ă (æ) AND ε (εɚ) (*cont'd*)

apparent	a parent	dally	dairy	clap	Claire
repack	repair	lack	lair	has	hairs
forbade	forbear	latter	laity	gap	Gary

It will be seen that since the sound of /εɚ/ represents the *r* in transition (see Chapter II) an exact parallel between words is not obtainable.

The student's own participation in composing such drills is eminently worth the time it takes. First, because he will drill more intelligently and therefore establish new patterns more firmly and quickly, and second, because it will give him a technique to apply to other areas where drill may be needed. The following remarkable example of empathy with the sounds of /æ/ and /εɚ/ was composed by a student.

The Mad Hatter sat and stormed
At the rat, who dozed on without a care
Of the Mad Hare's jabs and digging stabs,
The rodent slept, unaware.

"Alack! Alack! She'll never come back!"
Sobbed the Hare with a sorrowful groan.
When at last, to a slap, the rat woke from his nap
And uttered a horrified moan.

"Of what do you speak?
Oh whom do you shriek?
And why so aghast do you stand?"

The Hare with a sigh, his tear-drops did dry,
"It's about Alice of Wonderland."

Now thoroughly startled from out of his nap
The rat anxiously queried, "Did she have a mishap?"
"A mishap to us," cried the Hatter, "Alas!
Alice has gone back through the Looking Glass."

The rat straightway collapsed with a squeak,
And the Hare, in despair did the same with a shriek.

Another drill of this type which also shows the *r* in transition is a comparison between the diphthong /ɔɪ/ and the vowel /ɝ/. It will be noted that the words follow the order of articulation for consonants.

COMPARATIVE LIST /ɔɪ/ AND /ɝ/

oily	early	loin	learn
ointment	earned it	loiter	lurker
poise	purse	alley	alert
poison	person	soil	Searle
spoil	pearl	soy	sir
boys	burrs	despoil	disperse
boil	burly	choice	churn
moist	immersed	Joyce	Jersey
moiety	murder	joining	journeying
moisten	mercy	adjoin	adjourn
Des Moines	demur	coy	cur
Foy	fur	coil	curl
foil	furl	recoil	recur
foist	first	coin	colonel
voice	verse	goiter	girder
avoid	averred	hoity-toity	hurt eternally
invoice	inverse	ahoy	a "her"
toys	terse		
toil	turn		
Toynbee	turbine		
doit	dirt		
doily	dirty		
noise	nurse		

THE MOBILITY DRILL

Achieving lightness of utterance and mobility of the tongue at conversational speed is a very important aspect of drilling. It is often neglected on the general belief that once a student can make and hear the sound, he is ready to effect the transition to ordinary speech by himself. This is not the case, particularly when a common, everyday error is involved, such as the substitution of *dis, dem, dose* for *this, them* and *those*. Here is a buildup drill for flexibility in that sound, namely, the /ð/ in *there:*

Ask your students to suggest five simple words beginning with *b* such as:

BAT', BOAT', BIKE', BALL', BOY'

Encourage them to pronounce these words firmly and with strong emphasis. Then add the word *the,* maintaining the pattern of stress:

the BAT', the BOAT', the BIKE', the BALL', the BOY'

Substitute the words *to the* . . . , maintaining the pattern:

to the BAT', etc.

Be sure that the elision tɜ·ə is avoided. Continue to amplify the phrase, holding the pattern, but changing its rhythm:

from the . . .
there is the . . .   BAT' etc. . .
with and without the . . .
because of the . . .

Since your anchor words used only the first consonant of the alphabet there is plenty of room for the ambitious student to proceed!

EAR-TRAINING DRILLS

The natural sequence of drills in the speech clinic is ear, eye, and tongue — acoustic, kinesthetic, and motor. Ear training is not only first chronologically, but first in importance. It can be of several kinds:

1. A listening drill for the recognition of the sound by itself.
2. A listening drill for hearing the sound in comparison with other sounds (comparative drills).
3. A recognition drill to perceive and distinguish the sound as it occurs in written language.
4. Sophisticated listening to readers, records, and tapes for specific elements such as sounds, pauses, patterns of emphasis, as well as for general appreciation.

This is perhaps one of the most neglected aspects of clinic work since, without spending money for special equipment, it is the most difficult type of activity to implement. Ear-training experiences, however, are of great importance, and the clinician should do all in his power to introduce them.

DRILLING COMMON ERRORS

An area that needs constant reinforcement by drill is the correction of common errors. Such drills can be set up in many ways: as basic drills to begin or end the session, as comparative drills, mobility drills, or even as creative challenges. The adventures of hairy Harry and sad Sarah have been known to out-fiction the science fiction writers, to the accompaniment of occasional guffaws, which are therapeutically valuable in the speech clinic. Omissions; additions; substitutions; infantilisms; voicings and unvoicings; the glottal click; difficult consonant combinations such as the *dnt* in *couldn't*, or the *sts* and *sks* clusters; spelling anomalies like *qu, ng, -ed* final, and silent letters are all grist for this mill. Within the framework of our double purpose — the elimination of a specific fault, and the improvement in communicative skills — there is much room for many informal drills. To illustrate: You plan a drill to combat a common tendency to unvoice a final /z/ sound when it is spelled with an *s*. Begin by placing five common words on the board:

IS, DOES, WAS, HAS, GOES

Develop the drill by varying the routines:

a. Repeat the list several times.
b. Add one word, *it:* "It is . . . It does . . ." etc.
c. Double the words on themselves: "IS is IS" and "DOES is DOES," etc.
d. Add two words (Note the /s/ in *this*): "Is this IS? Is this DOES?," etc.

Note that each step is progressively more difficult. Such a drill can be completed in the first five minutes of the period if the students are trained to accept drills.

ILLUSTRATING A LEARNED SOUND

In this type of drill, the students give examples of the sound being studied. Let us say that we wish to practice a clear diphthong /aɪ/. First, the students listen to the sound pronounced by the clinician. They are then challenged to listen discriminatingly by indicating whether the sound as pronounced by the clinician is "right" or "wrong" in a series of correct and incorrect pronunciations such as: aɪ ɔɪ aɪ aɔɪ ʌɪ aɪ aɪ ɑɪ. Analyzing further, the clinician may use the symbol of railroad tracks, which he can draw on the blackboard in this way:

In this manner he shows the importance of the first element, especially when it "goes off the track." When the sound has been "set," the first student starts a "chain" with a phrase — "I try." The second student repeats the phrase and adds his own — "I try but I cry." The third picks up the last part and improvises — "I cry but I sigh." Combinations have been known to be both very apt and less than logical, but the main purpose has been served.

DRILL VS. REALITY

Knee-bending is not real movement and drilling is not speaking. It is good for both the clinician and the students to understand this. Whatever is drilled must be practiced and tested under normal — *i.e.*, speaking — conditions. The drills themselves will progress toward more complex constructions, but the final judgment of improvement will be made in a speaking situation.

Drills, as we have seen, will constitute a major part of the work of the speech clinic, leaving a lesser allotment of time for the presentation of theory. Where a clinic meets four or five times a week, it would be well to devote the equivalent of a period to the presentation of various concepts in speech improvement; where it meets only three times a week, a twenty-minute presentation should suffice. For speech clinics meeting only once a week, the clinician should concentrate on drill alone.

Every speech clinic, however, no matter how constituted, should encourage "speech talk" — current references to speech in newspapers, magazines, radio, TV and theater, related vocabulary, and personality evaluations involving speech. A clinician who is aware of the far-flung speaking world about him and adept at introducing material from it into the clinic will do much to widen the horizons of his students, without which there is very little lasting improvement in speech.

IV

Lisping and Lalling

APPROACHES TO THE CORRECTION OF LISPS

You now have a workable group of lispers. You are acquainted with them, more or less, individually — that is, you know what they expect from the speech clinic and whether they have major physical problems such as tongue-tie, irregular teeth, braces, hay fever, allergies, malocclusion, hearing loss, tongue abnormalities. In some cases you have sent students to the school doctor or to a clinic for a specific medical examination. A geographic tongue, for instance, generally indicates a vitamin deficiency, which is not in your province to treat, although its effect on speech is, of course, your concern. You have aroused the students' interest in speech improvement and have perhaps introduced some drills for muscular flexibility. You now wish to begin work on the correction of the lisp itself. A lisp can be defined as the blurring, exaggeration, distortion or misdirection of the airflow in articulating any of the sibilants, thus producing an unacceptable sound. Are you aware, however, that there are many ways of skinning this particular cat? A method that will work for one person may not be the best method for another. Let us call these methods "approaches" and see at what point each of our students produces an acceptable /s/ sound. A necessary aspect of any approach is sustaining naturalness and ease of performance. The use of a hand mirror so that the student may observe the positioning of the sound is important.

The First Approach

When the bite is average — that is, with some overbite, but not undershot and without open occlusion — a basic approach is from the normal bite position — that is, with the side teeth in occlusion as for biting or chewing. From this position, initiate a thin stream of air, letting it flow out in a median stream through the space between the upper and lower teeth. When the "feeling" of this flow has been set, add a small movement forward of the lower jaw, as if escorting the air forward. It is not necessary for the teeth to meet in front. In fact, in most cases, it is preferable that the lower teeth rest just behind the upper. The desideratum of this approach is that the student should get a sense of airflow under control, should feel friction, and should get an approximate /s/.

The Second Approach

In making a good /s/, the air must flow without interruption. A tongue that works too far forward (lingual protrusion) or is deprived of a resting place by teeth that slant in, or that is itself too large and meaty, must be directed to function farther back. The main body of the tongue will then rest farther back and permit the front of the tongue and tip of the tongue to move about freely and direct the airflow. In this, our second approach, instruct the student to pull the tongue back, using the back muscles of the tongue. The front of the tongue will instinctively rise and assume its natural position of rest. Draw the student's attention to the large amount of space behind the teeth. Then have him experimentally place the tip of the tongue on the gum ridge where it meets the upper teeth. In this position let him try a few *s* sounds, encouraging sharpness of enunciation. Explain that this is a preliminary approach to the next drill.

The Third Approach

A good /s/ and /z/ sound is made by a directed flow of air through a channel high in the mouth. Drawing the tongue back as in the second approach, the student lifts the sides of his tongue to his upper side teeth — that is, he presses the sides of his tongue against the inner sides of the teeth. Holding this position tenaciously, he adjusts his bite to a convenient position and permits the tip of the tongue to place itself easily near the upper gum ridge. In this position he initiates a small airflow, noting the immediate increase in sharpness.

Ricochet S

If the above approaches are not successful in achieving a reasonably correct /s/, we suggest two positions that often help produce it. Bouncing the /s/ off the /f/ — that is, the /fs/ blend — has been used very successfully in our clinics. Beginning with the sound of /f/, convert the airflow into an /s/. A second position that has been found to be useful is that of the /ts/ or /nz/ blend — that is, we use the gum-ridge position of the first sounds to direct the airflow into the preferred upper position in the blend. The teacher will recognize the truth that, although the latter position is the more sophisticated, it is not, per se, the best one to use. Only by trial and error can he find the one most suitable in a particular instance. For this reason, the teacher must have an arsenal of approaches and techniques.

The Open-Bite Lisp

In working to eliminate the lisp of a person with an open bite, the clinician must be prepared realistically to accept a less sharp emission. There will be, it must be noted, a great variation in precision depending upon a number of factors: the student's overall standard of articulation, the degree of slant of the teeth, and the shape and mobility of the tongue. Most often, the clinician will achieve best results by directing the student to aim for a low-point /s/. This is made by keeping the body of the tongue quite flat at the bottom of the mouth with the tongue-tip resting lightly behind the edge of the bottom teeth, where it controls the airflow and generates friction. Although the /s/ produced here lacks a certain clarity, it is entirely adequate. A good /s/ sound, however, can never be made with lip control. The student *must* try for some form of tongue control.

Eliminating the Lisps on /ʃ/, /ʒ/ and the Blends

Lisps are not confined to the /s/ or its cognate. Any of the sibilants or affricates may be distorted. For our purposes it may be stated, however, that the /ʃ/ is the fountainhead of the /ʒ/, /tʃ/ and /dʒ/ sounds. The /ʒ/ is merely the /ʃ/ voiced; the /tʃ/ is the /ʃ/ preceded by /t/; similarly, the /dʒ/ is the /ʒ/ preceded by /d/. What does this mean in the clinic? A person whose lisp includes any or all of these sounds may be told that he has only one sound to "learn," namely, the /ʃ/. Once he controls that sound, he need only voice it to get /ʒ/, move the tongue down from the /t/ position onto the /ʃ/ to get /tʃ/. In the same way, he needs only to move from the /d/ onto the /ʒ/ to get /dʒ/.

The essential element in achieving a good /ʃ/ is to exert pressure on the middle of the tongue as it presses against the sides of the teeth, with the tongue-tip down. When this position has been firmly established, draw the student's attention to the part played by the cheek walls and lips in shaping the /ʃ/. The cheek walls draw in as the lips are rounded and thrust forward. If the student cannot himself draw his cheeks in, the teacher may, with a gentle pressure of his thumb and middle finger, aid him. It is a matter of great encouragement to a student to be told that if he can form this one sound, he will be guaranteed the other three.

There are those, strangely, whose difficulty lies not with the primary /ʃ/ but exclusively with one or both of the blends. Let us assume there is a lisp on the /dʒ/ blend. In this case it is wise to go back to the primary /ʃ/, add voice, /ʒ/, and explain the movement of the tongue from the d position to the /ʒ/ position. Stress the fact that only the /ʒ/ is held. A drill like the following is useful at this stage:

- Intone the /ʒ/ for five slow beats, without stopping the sound:

  /ʒ/ /ʒ/ /ʒ/ /ʒ/ /ʒ/

- Repeat, lifting the tongue to the d position after beat two, hold, and continue in rhythm:

  /ʒ/ /ʒ/ /d/ hold /ʒ/ /ʒ/ /ʒ/

- Change the "lift" to follow beats one, three, and four, and finally, to precede beat one.

The student will realize that he is really producing the blend /dʒ/.

Evaluations

The result of these approaches at the very beginning of therapy should be to equip each student with the best /s/ sound he can make, that is, *with an acceptable /s/ sound*. Too many correction classes have taken as their final goal "the correction of the lisp." This is insufficient. Learning to make a good *s* sound is only preliminary. The greater part of the clinic time should be devoted to teaching:

- How to drill and how to compose drills.
- Drilling.
- That portion of phonetic theory that is related to the problems of the class.*
- A respect for and love of good speech wherever found. Readiness for self-improvement.

* Such topics as cognate confusion; omissions and additions; substitutions; slurring of sounds; the study of any individual sound; phonetic and unphonetic aspects of language; pronunciation of words; the functions of the schwa; comparative drills; stress within the word and phrase; nasality and denasalization; standards of speech — personal and professional.

- Elimination of personal speech habits that interfere with clear communication — inaudibility, lack of eye contact, poor breath support, involuntary gestures.
- Listening recognition, judgments.

When each student has made and heard his acceptable /s/ [/z/, /sh/, /zh/, /ch/, /dg/] sound, the class is ready to be launched on its term's work. This readiness constitutes the beginning, not the end product, of the speech clinic.

Drilling

All drill work is directed at muscular, aural, and oral acuity. In that sense it is like gymnastics, an analogy that is productive for the clinician. If the speech class is the language gymnasium, then it follows that the student may expect to exaggerate in flexing his muscles — if he knows that he is doing so. Early drilling must stress listening and looking.

SATURATION DRILLS

Initial /s/. No Other Sibilants or Blends

see, seaplane, seep, seem, seeming, seaweed, seed, cedar, seat, seating, seethe, seafood, scene, scenic, sear, seal, soak, secrete, secret, seagirt, sea gull; simple, simmer, symphony, sip, sipped, sibilant, sibyl, sift, sifter, sieve, civil, Sidney, sit-down, sit, sin, scintillate, sitter, sill, silly, syrup, sirrah, sick, sicken, sickening, signal, cigar; septic, semi-mute, semolina, sense, Sephardic, several, scent, senate, sell, seldom, self, serrate, serried, sect, sector, second, segment; Sarah; Sam, sample, salmon, sap, sapling, Sabbath, sabine, sapphire, saffron, Savarin, savvy, sat, satin, sadder, sadden, sand, sank, sanitary, salad, sallow, salve, salvia, Saracen, saraband, sack, saccharine, sag, sagamore; sue, soup, supine, soubrette, super, soon, sooth, soothe, suit, suitable, suiter, suet, sued, Sudan, Seule, sewer; soot, sooty; saw, sawmill, soften, sought, sawed, sauna, Saul, soar, sort, song, saunter; sob, sobbing, sop, sovereign, sophomore, sot, sod, sodden, sonnet, solder, solid, solemn, sorrow, sock, socket, soccer, soggy; psalm, saga, sergeant, sardonic, sari; sir, Serb, servant, sermon, serf, serfdom, serpent, certain, sirloin, serve, servile, circus; sum, summer, sub, sub-marine, sup, supper, supple, sough, suffer, suffix, suffocate, south-ern, sudden, subtle, Sunday, sunburn, sulk, sullen, sulky, suck, suckle; Savannah, severe, satanic, salute, saloon, sabbatical, silhouette, Socratic, soprano, solidity, semantic, sublime, submit, sultana, supplant, supply; say, same, sable, Sabine, safe, safety, save, Savior, sated, sadism, sale, sailor, salable, sane, saint, sake, sacred; sigh, Simon, simonize, Siam, Siberia, siphon, scythe, side, sidle, sided, site, cited, sign, signed, silentium, silent, sire, siren, psyche, Saigon; sew, sewn, somatic, sober, soap, soviet, sofa, sewed, soda, sole, solely, solar, so real, so new, so-called, Saudi, sound, sour, south; soy, soil, Sawyer

Final /s/. No Other Sibilants or Blends

peace, niece, Maurice, lease, fleece, crease, grease, geese; miss, remiss, premise, penance, furnace, practice, malice, preface, tennis, Dennis, menace, Phyllis, Mavis, Morris, Prudence, kiss, crevice; fence, tense, cadence, mess, immense, pence, Bess, con-fess, caress, less, guess, Hortense, yes; pass, pants, bass, mass, lass, class, crass, gas; Grace, case, mace, pace, base, face, dais, Thrace, lace, race, trace; ice, mice, Weiss, suffice, vice, thrice, twice, dice, entice, lice, rice, price, trice; moose, deuce, noose, loose, footloose, ruse, use, goose; puss; dose, close, gross; moss, boss, enforce, divorce; toss, doss, loss, Ross, cross, gorse; us, muss, bus, pus, fuss, thus, plus, truss, Russ, cuss, Gus; Merce, purse, verse, terse, curse

Medial /s/. No Other Sibilants or Blends

piecemeal, desegregate, leasing, increasing; pistol, whistle, fistula, felicity, duplicity, reminiscent; pestle, wrestle, estimate; fasten, nasty, lassitude, vacillate, classic; viceroy, tricycle, icicle; rooster, booster, Tucson; Worcester; pester, closer, roaster; Austria, toss-ing, faucet, paucity; imposter, roster, ossify; nursing, bursting, thirsty; tussle, bustle, bustling

/s/ *Combinations*

All /s/ combinations must be drilled. They are: *sm, sp, sw, spl, spr, -ps, st, sn, sl, sk, str, -fs, -ths, -st, -ts, -ns, -ls, -sk, -ks.* A productive form of drill contains the sound in initial, final, and medial positions. The following is a drill for the /st/. Other lists can easily be composed by teachers or students:

/st/ (initial)	/st/ (final)	/st/ (medial)
step	pest	pestilence
stew	west	western
stammer	mast	masthead
stab	baste	basting
staff	fast	fasting
Steven	vest	vestment
stint	test	testing
study	dust	dust-mop
steno	nest	nesting
still	list	listing
stallion	last	lastly
store	roast	roasting
stair	raced	race-time
stack	cast	casting
stoke	cost	costly
stuck	gust	disgusting
stogy	ghost	ghostly

Transition to Conversational Speech

Just as the modern gym class does when it shifts from gymnastics to dancing and other forms of real movement, the speech clinic must provide for a carry-over into conversational speech. This transition is not immediate. A new pathway in the gray matter of the brain supplants the old, and the new sound concept becomes surer until finally it is automatic. A transition drill that can be assigned at regular intervals is the prepared paragraph. The student selects a paragraph from material he uses — textbook,

41

newspaper, book of literature — copies it into his speech note-book, and underlines all its sibilants and blends. He then practices them within the phrase in which they occur, consciously watching the articulations involved. He first reads the paragraph slowing down for the sibilants and blends, and then normally, letting the *sips, ships, chips,* and *gyps* fall where they may. Here is a sample paragraph [1] analyzed:

> You should be at ease in a speech class. You should know all your classmates well so that you can carry on discussions and practice sessions in a friendly, relaxed atmosphere. If you are all friends, you can offer helpful suggestions to one another, knowing that they will be accepted gladly. When you and your classmates are well acquainted, you can work together happily and effec-tively. Your teacher also needs to know you if he is to help you to become a better person and speaker.

The following phrases containing the sibilants from the above paragraph can be practiced:

/ʃ/   /z/   /s/ /tʃ/   /s/   /ʃ/

You should be at ease in the speech class. You should know

/s/   /s//s/   /s/ /ʃ/ /z/   /s/

your classmates so that you can carry on discussions and practice

/s//ʃ/ /z/   /kst/   /s/   /z/

sessions in a friendly relaxed atmosphere. If you are all friends,

/dʒ//tʃ//z/

you can offer helpful suggestions to one another, knowing that

---

[1] Griffith, Nelson and Stasheff, *Your Speech,* p. 1. Reprinted by permission of the Publisher, Harcourt, Brace & World.

/ks/ /s/ /s/ /tʃ/

they will be accepted by your classmates. Your teacher also n̲ ̲ ̲

/z/ /s/

your cooperation if he is to help you to be a better person and

/s/

speaker.

Passages from the students' everyday reading provide as much practice as they will ever need. Improvement will be noted immediately, and the student should be made aware of it. The clinician may have to remind himself that correction is a process, and the ability to make the correct sound in isolation is achieved faster than the carry-over into speaking and reading.

APPROACHES TO THE CORRECTION OF LALLING

Lalling is the generic term for the defective pronunciation of the /l/ and /r/ sounds. Such mispronunciations are associated by the listener with infantilism and are generally a burden to the speaker. From the point of view of original cause, however, the laller is rarely to blame. The mispronunciation may stem from as remote a source as having been bottle-fed too long as a baby. It may be associated with a general muscular laxness, or it may — and this is the first concern of the speech teacher — be the outcome of a tongue-tie. Now it is perhaps presumptive to suppose that a physical condition such as tongue-tie can exist in a person of such mature age, but hardly a year has passed that we have not found several among the children attending the speech clinic.

Cases of suspected tongue-tie should be referred to the school doctor, who will make his recommendation to a private physician or clinic. The clipping of the frenum is a minor operation. Retraining of the tongue usually begins a week or two later. If, however, there is no ascertainable physical cause, and consideration has also been given to a possible hearing deficiency or to imitation, training for the correct production of the sound may begin.

Let us consider the properties of the first of these sounds, the /l/ sound. This consonant (the only one of its kind in the language) is pronounced with the airflow coming over the sides of the tongue, the tongue-tip touching the upper gum ridge lightly. Hence the sound is known as lateral. It is unique in other ways — for the fact that it is produced without friction or plosion, and so, like the nasal sounds, legato in feeling; it is capable of a vibrato quality which gives the language great beauty; it has variety within its phoneme, that is, there is a clear /l/ in the initial position in the word, or after an initial consonant — for example, *light* and *blight*, and a dark /l/ in the final position or before a final consonant, *wall* and *walled*. It is subject to progressive assimilation in combinations like *plead* and *clean* where it is partially voiceless. It is therefore an important asset to good speech and well worth the effort to improve it.

The teacher begins the training for the correct production of the /l/ sound by establishing an aural concept of the sound. The student must hear the difference between a tip-tongue /l/ and a mid-air, pursed-lip sound, the latter resembling a/w/. The teacher may be forgiven if he adds a bit of stigma to the unpleasant effect of the mispronunciation if this gives impetus to the student's desire to improve. Practice consists of:

1. Hearing the sound accurately. Ear training ranges from simple judgments — "a good /l/" or "a bad /l/" — to identifying the substitution.
2. Lifting the tongue and placing the tip on the gum ridge, observing the correct position in a mirror.

3. Sensing the muscular pressure which flattens the tip (dark /l/) and learning to drop the middle of the tongue and form a trough through which the air is expelled over the sides.
4. Drills in all positions and in various rhythms as described below.

The Basic Drill

This is the same drill used to initiate any unit. The /l/ sound is pronounced before and after the three basic vowels /i/, /eɪ/ and /aɪ/ in single, double, and triple utterance and in blends: *pl, bl, fl, sl, shl, spl, kl, gl*. The combinations *-lp* (*whelp*), *-lb* (*bulb, Wilbur*), *-lf* (*shelf*), *-lv* (*shelve*), *-lth* (*wealth*), *-lt* (*welt*), *-ld* (*weld*), *-dl* (*needle*), *-tl* (*little*), *-lk* (*welk*), *-rl* (*whirl*), *-lts* (*waltz*), *-lz* (*wills*), *-zl* (*muzzle*), *-chl* (*Rachel*), *-lch* (*belch*), *-ldg* (*bilge*) *and -ngl* (*angle*) should be drilled only as found in language, that is, after the vowels.

SATURATION DRILLS (THREE POSITIONS)

Initial

leak, least, leap, leave, lead (v), leash, Lethe, lethal, lease, Lisa, leader, leaf, league, legal, liege, legion, Lima, lean, leer, Leon, leech, leisure, leeward, lesion; lick, list, lip, live (v), lid, listen, lizard, lift, limb, lint, liver, liquor, Lisbon, lisp; let, leaven, lest, leper, leopard, lever, led, lethargy, less, left, leg, legacy, lemon, Lent, Lebanon, legend; lake, lave, laid, lathe, lazy, lame, lain, labor, label, lace, lading, ladle, late, later, lady, lay; lair; lack, lab, lad, laugh, lag, lamb, laminate, lantern, land, lap, Larry, last, lash, latch, latter, Latin, lavender, Lazarus, lax, lavatory; like, license, light, lie, lied, life, libel, limelight, line, liar, lighten, lively; loot, loop, lewd, loom, loon, lure, loose, lose, Lulu, louver; look; lobe, load, locate, local, loaf, loge, loam, lonely, lope, Lois, low, loathe; Laura, laud, laudable, lawn, law, loss, laurel, laundry, lord; Lloyd, loiter, loin; lock, lot, lobby, log, logarithm, logic,

Lonny, lozenge, lodge, longitude; lark, lava, lingerie, llama, Lana; lout, loud, lounge, lousy; luck, lunch, lush, London, love, lust; learn, lurk, lurch

Final

eel, deal, feel, heal, keel, meal, kneel, peel, reel, seal, teal, steal, veal, we'll, real; ill, imbecile, dill, fill, hill, kill, mill, nil, shrill, civil, pill, rill, sill, till, still, villa, will, frill, chill, thrill; fell, Mel, knell, pell-mell, sell, tell, well, Noel, shell, jell, quell; quail, sale, bail, pail, fail, frail, whale, mail, nail, kale, impale, vale, retail, they'll; Hal, Pal, gal, Sal, shall; pile, bile, while, file, vile, tile, dial, guile, reconcile, style, I'll, Kyle, rile, Lyle, mile, Nile, pile, delight; pool, cool, stool, drool, duel, fool, spool, school, ghoul, who'll, jewel, cruel, tool, mule, renewal, puerile, rule; wool, pull, bull, full; pole, bowl, dole, coal, soul, foal, toll, shoal, Joel, role, knoll, mole, stole, troll, scroll; Paul, ball, wall, maul, fall, thrall, tall, stall, shawl, call, gall, protocol; coil, boil, foil, Hoyle, soil, oil, royal, toil; doll; earl, pearl, curl, churl, girl, Merle, whirl; dull, cull, skull, hull, gull, mull, null

Medial

elite, lee, jubilee, delete, alley; civilization, elicit, elixir, Melinda, relinquish, billet, million, polish, children, relive, religion, unlit; cellist, prelate, realm, Ella, elf, delve, Stella, element, epilepsy, relent, belly, Kelly, helping, jelly, Nelly, impelled, pellet, telephone, legend, selling; baled, mailed, wailed, failed, failing, veiling, ailing, nailing, nailed, regaled, railed, mutilate, retailed, sailor, salesman, salable; ballyhoo, palate, retaliate, palatable, talent, fallible, Valhalla, jalousie, callous, mallet, calendar, challenge, malnutrition, allergy, rally, ballot, valley, talisman; bilingual, silent, enlighten, Elijah, childish, filed, filing, dialed, dialing, beguiling, smiling, delighted, reviled, whiled; pooled, balloon, cooling, cooled, grueling, bejeweled, voluminous, mulish, resolute, refueled; pulling, fully, woolen, woolly; Polish, bowled, polled, coldly, doled, folding, folded, golden, beholden, wholly,

46

lolled, molded, molding, revolt, revolting, tolled, tolling, rolled, olden, floated; Baltic, walnut, mauled, vault, vaulted, vaulting, fallen, hauled, halted, cauliflower, calling, Pawling, Raleigh, stalling, smallish, Walter; doily, boiling; golly, folly, holly, holler, volley, polish, resolved; earlier, furled, girlish, purled, purling, surly, Shirley, churlish, whirling, Merlin, Alfred Lunt, Allan Ludden.

Combinations

The so-called difficult combinations, /pl/, /bl/, /kl/, /gl/, /fl/, and /spl/, will lose their difficulty for the student when he understands that he holds the /l/ sound while pronouncing the previous one. When drilling, therefore, he does not take his tongue away from the /l/ position, but works to move quickly from the first sound to the intoning of the /l/, which begins, in thought, simultaneously with the first sound.

The sibilant combinations /sl/, /shl/, and /chl/ are somewhat different in timing since the airflow must be controlled at the exact point of contact, the gum ridge, required by the /l/. In these, the sibilant is shortened, cut off as it were, while the flattened tip clamps into place as if sucked onto it by a vacuum.

The dental plosive combinations are truly more difficult especially for those who have substituted avoidance pronunciations such as the glottal click /se?l/ for *settle* or for those who insert a vowel where none exists (/setɪl/ or /setəl/). What actually transpires in the pronunciation of /tl/ and /dl/ is that the tongue-tip takes and holds the position for /t/, but does not enunciate it. The /t/ and /l/ are pronounced simultaneously. The emission is lateral, as for the /l/ and plosive, as for the /t/. Some people favor a one-sided plosion. The combination is well taught in slow motion, the teacher checking for the moment of contact of the /t/, which is held for a brief second, the student then proceeding as indicated above. Recommended drills and suggestions for composing drills on these combinations will be given later in the chapter.

47

Malpronunciations; Substitutions

Problems with the /l/ sound do not stop here. It is often replaced by either an /r/ or /w/ sound — "The Wady of Shawott" or "The Rady of Sharott." It is these mispronunciations that are popularly associated with infantilism. In these cases, assuming that he has checked for physical causes, the teacher should talk with the student and with his parents to familiarize himself with the speech history: At what age did the child begin to talk? Was he encouraged to use baby talk and up to what age did he use it? Was he bottle-fed? Up to what age? The clinician can then judge how ingrained the problem is. Retraining then begins, as always, with the ear, with hearing the difference between the substandard sound and the correct one. The question of the recognition of the correct sound is not one of a single experience. A graded series of practice exercises with innumerable choices should be initiated. The use of a tape recorder and prerecorded recognition drills with answer sheets for student use will help immeasurably. These exercises are followed by kinesthetic and visual observations, that is, work with a mirror and observation of a model speaker.

The student is now ready for the series of graded drills on words. It is interesting to observe that some students find one position of the /l/ easier to pronounce than another. The teacher carefully notes successes and difficulties for reference in future drilling. From these drills he progresses to phrases, avoiding excessively long and complicated ones. Requiring a person who has difficulty with a sound to pronounce complexes whose meaning is subordinated to the tapestry of sound is not only educationally unsound, but cruel. Thus, sentences like "Little Lord Fauntleroy beguiled the artful, lolling cannibal" are to be avoided. In line with the theory that students should be taught to compose drills of their own, the following simple patterns are given. Where the purpose is to achieve muscular movement, it is not necessary to burden either the student or teacher with sense-orientated matter.

Initial /l/

look to the left, listen for the lyric, live and let live, labor of love, like lakes of grain, loora loora lay, lease on life, lesson in logic, lackluster, last but not least, Laura likes Latin, loose and lose, lot of licorice, Do you like lab work?

Final /l/

will (say as a phrase)	leave, live, love, like, lick, lack
shall	look, loiter, laud, labor, listen
he'll	learn, bill, sell, kill, call, cool
she'll	toil, tell, furl, bale, rile, toll
they'll	mull, enroll, appeal, refill

Medial /l/

always	alone, aloof, alight, aligned
frequently	delighted, altruistic, old, filling
seldom	silly, calloused, illogical, churlish
definitely	earlier, furled, curly
troubled and	wild, lovely, puzzled, heckling
	forlorn, ill-tempered, ill-willed
	calculating, childish

/pl/ and /bl/ initial

please, plead; plinth, Plymouth; pleasure, plenty, pledge; Plato, plait, play, placate, place, plane; plateau, plaid, plaster, plaque, placid, placard, planet, platform, plan; ply, pliers, plight; Pluto, plume, plural, pleurisy; pluck, plum; plosion, plover; plausible, Plautus; plop, plot, plod; plaza; plum, plunk, pluck, plush, plumber, plus

bleak, bleary, bleed; blink, blister, bliss; blend, bless, bled; blade, Blake, blaze, blatant; blare; blast, blanket, black, blank; blight, blind, blithe; blue, bloomer, bloom; blow, bloat; blot, blossom, block; blarney, blasé; blur, blurt, blurb; blush, blubber, blood

/pl/-/bl/ *final*

steeple, people; stipple, pimple, ripple, nipple; maple, papal, staple; chapel, ample, sample, apple, dapple; disciple; scruple, hoople; topple; purple; couple, supple

feeble, nibble, kibble; rebel, pebble, treble; able, enable, fable, table, sable, Mabel, cable; amble, rabble, babble; Bible, tribal; ruble, connubial; global, mobile, Sobel, noble; foible; hobble, wobble, job'll; verbal, herbal; bubble, rubble, crumble, humble, fumble, stumble, bumble, rumble

/pl/-/bl/ *medial*

peopled, replete, complete; discipline, pimpled, crippled, applicable, replica, implicit; replenish, unpleasant; replaceable, fabled, shapeless, implacable; unplanned, replastered; pipeline, implied, supplied, soupless; showplace, hopeless; applaud; employ, deploy; explore; toppled; purpled; troubled

/pl/-/bl/ *approximated*

palpable, epilepsy, capillary, opal, jubilee, tarpaulin, polite, Mobile, Impala, palace, pallid, palate, peerless, pelican, pellet, pellucid, pelvis, pelt, pilfer, pilgrim, pillow, pilot, polar, political, polygon, polyp, pullet, pulley, pulmonary

/kl/-/gl/ *initial*

clean, clear, cliché, cleave, clique, cleat; cling, click, cliff, Clinton, clipped; cleft, clemency, clerical, kleptomaniac, clever, clench; claim, clay; Claire; clad, clam, clannish, clap, class, clash, clatter, clavicle; climb, climate, client, climax, clue; clothe, cloak, close, clove, clover; claw, Santa Claus, clause, Claude, cloy, cloister; clock, clot, clod, clonic, closet, clobber; cloud, cloy, clown; clerk, clergy; club, cluster, cluck, clutter gleam, Gleason, glean, glee; glib, glimpse, glimmer, glint, glisten, glitter, glycerine; Glen; glade, glacier, glaze; glare, glaring; glad, gladiator, glamour, glance, gland, glass; glider, gliding; gloom, glucose, glue, gluten; glorious, glorify, gloss; globe, gloat, glow; glottis, glove, glum, glutton

/kl/-/gl/ final

beagle, legal, regal, treacle; giggle, mingle, jingle, dingle, pickle, nickel, wiggle, fickle, mickle, chicle, sickle; shekel, deckle, heckle, Jekyl, freckle, speckled; bagel; fragile, triangle, taggle, mangle, tangle, haggle, spangle, tackle, cackle, shackle, dangle, wrangle, wangle, jangle, jackal, spackle; cycle, Michael; ducal, frugal; yokel, local, coke'll; cockle; circle, gurgle; buckle, knuckle, suckle, chuckle

/kl/-/gl/ medial and approximated

bakelite, recollect, bicycled, cuckold, Chagall, ganglion, jugular, chocolate, disclose, proclaim

/fl/ initial

flee, fleece, fleet, fleeting; flicker, flimsy, flinch, fling, flit, flint, flippant; flesh, flexible, fleck, fledgling, Flemish; flare; flake, flagrant, flame, flavor; flack, flabby, flaccid, flag, flank, flagellate, flap, flannel, flash, flask, flat, flatter, flax; flight, fly, flier; fluent, flue, fluid, fluke, fluorescent, flute; flow, float; floss, flaunt, floor, Flora, floral; flock, flog, flop, Florida, flotsam; flirt, flourish; flood, fluff, flunk, flung, flurry, flush, fluster, flutter, flux; flounder, flounce, flour, flout

/fl/ final

piffle; sleigh full, playful; careful, baffle, raffle, staff'll; Eiffel, stifle, rifle, knife'll, trifle; rueful, shoe full, fruitful; bowl full, woeful, soulful; awful, thoughtful; joyful; waffle; duffle, shuffle, truffle, muffler

51

/fl/-/vl/ medial and approximated

inflation, inflame, affluent, afflicted, influence, muffled, profligate, baffling, wallflower, Wellfleet, Teflon, deflector, deflate, deftly, awfully, lifeless, lifeline, lively, reflect, raffling, real freak, relax, rifleman, roof leak; unruffled, safflower, softly, solfeggio, safely, shelving, shiftless, scaffold, silver, sylphlike, selfless, sylvan, shuffled, trifled, carefully, coughless

/sl/ initial

sleep, sleazy, sleeve, sleet, sleek; slick, slip, slim, sliver, slither, slink, slit, slid, sling; slept, slender, sled, sledge; slave, slain, slate, slay, slake; slab, slap, slam, slat, slack, slag, slash, slander, slang; slime, slide, slice, slight, slighter, sly; sloop, slew, sleuth, sluice; slow, slowly, slope, Sloan, slogan, slothful; slaw; slot, slobber; Slav; slouch, slur, slurring, slumber, slush, slough, slut, slovenly, sludge, slug, slump

/sl/-/zl/ final

measles, weasel, Teazle, diesel; bristle, whistle, missile, fizzle, thistle, Quisling, sizzle, frizzle, grizzled, tinsel; trestle, pencil, vessel, wrestle, nestle, Cecil; nasal, Hazel; castle, razzle-dazzle, basil; Feisal; fuse'll, refusal; causal, dorsal, morsel; jostle, nozzle, fossil, docile, apostle; parcel, metatarsal; reversal, rehearsal; puzzle, hustle, rustle, guzzle, tussle, muscle, mussel

/sl/ (zl, zhl, shl, dgl) medial and approximated

paisley, cheese'll spoil, it's like this, versatile, it's later, this'll do it, bestial, special, casual, crucial, wassail, desolate, feasible, solicit, Celeste, keys'll drop, vaseline, chaise longue, the farce'll close

Substitutions for the /r/

The mispronunciation of the /r/, like that of the /l/, is suggestive of infantilism. Like the latter, the /r/ has great variety in its phoneme, both in American speech and inter-linguistically (see Chapter II). This mispronunciation can be the result of tongue-tie or of lack of muscle tone. It can be the end product of the sluggishness caused by a large, unwieldy, or flabby tongue, or of habits contracted in babyhood.

The r, as we have seen, has several pronunciations in American speech depending on its position in the word or phrase. Let us review them here: As a single initial consonant in the word *rise* it has full consonantal value and is made with the tongue-tip curled back, lifting toward the working ridge while the middle of the tongue tenses against the side teeth without, however, grooving. The sound is made by the friction of the vocalized air passing through. Although it is a voiced sound without a voiceless cognate, it is pronounced at least partially unvoiced as the second part of a voiceless-voiced pair (progressive assimilation) — *prize*. As the last sound in the word it has, through a process of streamlining for over 500 years, been assimilated into the preceding vowel in several ways: where it has become part of the schwa, as in General American pronunciation /ɪɚ, ɛɚ, ɔɚ, ʊɚ/, or dropped completely /ɪə, ɛə, ɔə, ʊə/ it has formed new diphthongs, called the falling diphthongs because the second element has a lower tongue position than the first; before another final or medial consonant (*hoard, hoarding*) it is often not pronounced at all, or, as in General American, blended into the vowel, which is then pronounced in the inverted (/r/ type) position. In these pronunciations it ceases to exist as a consonant, since the "inverted" vowel is pronounced in a single position without additional movement of the tongue. A liaison /r/ is used where the final r is followed by a word beginning with a vowel — "The chore is hard" /ðə tʃɔɚɪz hɑɹd/. It has been our experience that it is better to require the General American standard in the pronunciations above with students who have difficulty with the sound of /r/ even though it may appear illogical to do so. If, having mastered the pronunciation, they decide to drop the /r/ sound where it is possible to do so, they will be surer of a clear and correct vowel.

Correcting Mispronunciations

The most common mispronunciation of /r/ is the substitution of an approximate /w/ for the /r/. The procedures for correcting it follow the same schedule as for the /l/: aural recognition, positioning experimentation (visual and kinesthetic approach), and graded drills. In forming the /r/, it is necessary for the student to learn to raise the front of the tongue and point it toward the back. This is best done from the normal bite position in the following steps:

1. Direct the student to place his tongue-tip on the upper gum and draw it back along the palate until it loses contact with the palate. This is now the correct position for an American /r/ sound.

2. He holds this position, remembering that the teeth are in light contact, and intones first *er* and then *her*. Continue, alternating *er* and *her*.

3. Repeat the above, parting the teeth slightly and still consciously placing the tongue in the correct position.

4. He learns to move into the /r/ position by pronouncing different vowels followed by *er*, thus:

   /i/ . . . *er*; /eĭ/ . . . *er*; /aĭ/ . . . *er*

   and so on through ten or more different vowels. At first the student makes a decided break between the vowel and the *er*, then he blends the two, being conscious, the while, of the movement of his tongue.

5. He learns to pronounce words ending in *er* following the voiced consonant /z/. He does the same with /ð/.

   buzzer, freezer, teaser, wiser, rosier, hazier, trouser, razor, easier, loser, appeaser, visor,

   weather, bother, Willa Cather, rather, tether, mother, father, brother, whither, heather

   (This step should be done in two parts, the first time

54

holding the /z/ or /ð/ until the tongue is almost in position for the *er;* the second time doing the same at a normal rate.)

By now the student should have a good concept of the sound of /r/ and is ready to use drills for fluency and mobility. These are easy to improvise using patterns like the following:

READ, RIP, RAID, RIDE, RUSH   Read one, read two, read three, read four, Rip one, etc.

The ROOM, RIVER, DRESS, BUREAU is

high,	low
wide,	narrow
long,	short
gray,	green

Contrastive lists are useful for both ear training and drill:

/l/-/r/ contrastive

lead – read, leach – reach, leak – reak, leap – reap, lean – ream, leal – real, legal – regal, leer – rear, leasehold – resold; lip – rip, lid – rid, livid – rivet, liquor – rigor, limb – rim, list – wrist, lick – Rick, liver – river, lift – rift, link – rink, lament – repent, linger – wringer; left – reft, lend –rend, lent – rent, lest – rest, let – Rhett, level – revel, leveler – reveler, lessen – resin, letch – wretch, Leonard – Renard, lex – Rex; laze – raze, lay – ray, lave – rave, lace – race, lacing – racing, lake – rake, late – rate, lading – raiding, lane – rain; lap – rap, laughter – rafter, lack – rack, lather – rather, lamb – ram, land – ran, lassie – rascal, language – wrangle, lath – wrath, lank – rank, lag – rag, latch it – rachet, lash – rash, lamp – ramp; lair – rare; lie – rye, lied – ride, life – rife, lined – rind, lithe – writhe, light – right, lion – Ryan, lyre – wryer; Lou – rue, loose – roost, loot – root, lewd – rude, loom – room;

55

look – rook; low – row, lower – rower, load – road, loam – roam, lobe – robe; law – raw, loss – Ross; lock – rock, lob – rob, lodger – Roger, lot – rot, lung – rung, lush – rush, lust – rust; Willy – weary, lily – leery, tooling – touring, telling – tearing, peeling – peering, pailing – paring, Pawling – pouring, sealed – seared, shield – sheared, filing – firing, build – beard, baled – bared, chilled – cheered, scald – scored, scowled – scoured, dilly – dearly, failed – fared, failing – faring, filing – firing, galling – goring, hauled – hoard, Hallie – Harry, hailed – haired, jelly – Jerry, Carlton – carton, call – core, climb – crime, close – crews, clip – crib, clan – cram, Julie – jury, clew – crew, glue – grew, O'Malley – Oh! marry!, molten – Morton, kneeling – nearing, polling – pouring, ceiling – searing, stealing – steering, tiling – tiring, tailing – tearing, willing – wearying, walling – warring, wailing – wearing, bleeding – breeding, blew – brew, blight – bright, boiled – Boyardee, flitter – fritter

All drills should be followed by normally paced readings, following suggestions made for the lisp.

We often find students of foreign extraction, notably Chinese, French, German, Israeli, and Italian in our clinics. All but the last have considerable trouble in converting their form of /r/ into ours. Speakers of Chinese background often confuse it with the /l/ (*fried rice* becomes *flied lice*). The French r sound is made by constricting the throat passage and forcing the air against the soft palate with the back of the tongue raised. The German *r* sound is pronounced still further back, although the glottis is not as constricted. Before embarking on a program of correction, the Chinese student should be given a careful period of ear training to distinguish the /l/ from the /r/. With French, German, and Israeli students work for frontal placement, by connecting the /r/ to front-placed consonants and vowels. The combinations *pr br, tr, dr, fr,* and *str* should be used with /i/, /eĭ/, and /aɪ/.

preen	praise	prize
breeze	braise	bride
trees	trace	tries
dream	dray	dry
freeze	phrase	fries
street	straight	strife

The addition of an /r/, especially a liaison /r/, where none exists is an intellectual misconception and is considered a vulgarism (*idear of, drawring room, lawr office, Georgiar,* and *Alabamar*). It is a very human feeling, however, to dislike being left open-mouthed at the end of a word, as one is between *law* and *office*. A liaison /r/ makes the transition more bearable. Nevertheless, good usage will not sanction it.

V

Improving the Use of the Voice

———————◆———————

Students are recommended to the high school speech clinic for a variety of voice defects and disorders: inaudibility, overloud voice, harshness and stridencies, breathiness, nasality (rhinolalia), denasalization, monotone speech, and that ever-present complaint from well-meaning teachers, "There's something funny about ——'s voice; I wish you'd listen to it." Of course, you will listen to him, as you do to every student, noting all elements which might have some bearing: general effectiveness of the voice in communication, projection, accompanying mannerisms, use of breath, intonation pattern, and even mispronunciations. So-called faulty voices have sometimes proven to be self-conscious lallers, or group-shy speakers, afraid or unaccustomed to using eye contact.

The clinician will have to be particularly careful in listening to and checking out the physical history of students recommended for faulty voice. There are four major areas that are, in themselves, so decisive that they must be evaluated before any therapy is undertaken.

First, the teacher must be aware of the syndromes of deafness and hearing loss, which may evidence themselves in a blurring or loss of the sibilants or of other voiceless consonants (misarticulation on high-frequency sounds), amateurish lipreading, an attenuated voice range, facial grimaces, and occasionally, antisocial behavior. Where the teacher has the smallest suspicion of hearing loss, he should refer the student for an audiometric evaluation.

Second, in cases of harshness or grating voice where no apparent physical condition such as laryngitis or abused voice ("football" voice and, these days, the cigarette-parched voice) seems to exist, a thorough throat examination should be recommended. A word of caution: The family doctor's general examination is not adequate. The clinician must specify and arrange for a nose, ear, and throat examination and ask that a report be sent to him. The clinician will have to know specifically whether conditions such as the following exist: nodules on the cords, inflamed vocal folds, tonsils, polyps, adenoidal growths, or possible paralysis of one or both of the vocal cords.

Third, nasality (hyper-rhinolalia) must be checked out in particular ways. To begin with, distinguish between it and denasalization (hypo-rhinolalia). Then inquire about conditions which may be known to the student such as asthma, hay fever, allergies, sinus condition, history of colds or mouth breathing (ask if the oral cavity is particularly dry in the morning), and repaired cleft, for which you will obtain details of the operation.

Fourth, the clinician should check the shape of the palatal arch to see if it is vaulted; he should evaluate the movement of the soft palate, noting in addition the possible absence of a uvula, a condition that we have seen a number of times.

All of the above may be causal or contributing factors to a voice problem.

THE STORY OF NAN

A very touching case, testifying to the importance of critical listening, recently came within our experience. The authors attended the yearly seminars of the Montefiore Hospital Cleft Palate Rehabilitation Center in New York City, where specialists in medicine, psychology, psychiatry, dentistry, orthodonture, surgery, and speech therapy reported on their joint experiences, findings, and conclusions. When we first saw Nan at sixteen she was a tall gaunt-looking child with wild hair and unhappy eyes. She had not, however, been neglected. Her history included a tonsillectomy and adenoidectomy at the age of two, and three years of speech therapy at what was formerly the National Hospital for Speech Disorders. From the age of six she was in a group for speech therapy at school, and at fourteen she had a year of individual therapy at the Speech and Hearing Clinic of City College, New York. None of this therapy had resulted in any appreciable change, but, now a student in high school, she was still trying to improve her voice. A noticeable "echo" quality of the nasality convinced us that the explanation would probably be physical. In spite of her history of speech therapy we felt justified in this assumption. A referral to the Montefiore Rehabilitation Center and the subsequent evaluation revealed a hidden, or submucous cleft and congenital short palate! The recommendation of a pharyngeal flap operation was approved by the parents and an early date was set. When next we saw Nan, her hair was appropriately and modestly combed, and the wild gleam in her eyes was subdued. She was confident that constructive help was on the way. It can be stated categorically that whenever one hears offensive nasal components in a child's voice, the presence of organic disorder should be seriously suspected. As far as possible in such cases, the teacher should obtain a valid differential diagnosis, including not only the judgment of a speech pathologist but of a physician as well. The story of Nan also shows the necessity for the skilled teacher to be on the alert for psychological overlay as well as physical malfunctions.

A POINT OF VIEW

Now, having recommended a thorough voice examination for a number of the students referred for voice therapy, we would like to present a second point of view, which may seem like backtracking. A judgment has been made about voice. A student is recommended for therapy. How accurate, objective, or scientific are these judgments? How kind are they? How valid? How practicable? How widely accepted? Suppose you had advised Louis Armstrong not to attempt to sing with his quality of voice? In some "objective" ways you would have been justified, yet the world would have lost a delightful performer who knows how to blend rhythmic nuances and open vowel tones and warm them by the glow of his smile into memorable interpretation . . . "Hello, Dolly!"

Since the voice is only one element of the composite we call personality, a characteristic that will mar one person's voice will not necessarily mar another's. Take, for instance, the question of nasality. There are parts of the country where it is indigenous, where it recalls the great plains, the distances, the woman at the door calling downfield, "Boys, come and get it!" There is, on the other hand, the nasal whine of the person who is continuously disgruntled with the world, the nasality of simple tiredness, and that of a seemingly congenital lack of interest. Tensions of city living, its noises and speed, can induce temporary or permanent nasality. These observations apply as well to harshness and stridencies. That such things exist, that they may need clinical attention, one cannot deny, but one must recognize that they exist in a context of checks and balances and do not carry with them an invariable and automatic onus. We consider this point of view essential philosophy for the clinician working in a large heterogeneous city school as opposed to, for example, a homogeneous finishing school. We are a pluralistic society of many strains. If the teacher affirms a broad philosophy, he will find that the tolerance of differences — the recognition of the need for individual evaluation that his students will acquire — is a valuable educational tool, as well as sound philosophy.

A STARTING PROCEDURE

In the voice clinic the teacher is in very close partnership with his students, but unless the student hears for himself what is being criticized in his voice and what he ought to strive for, and unless he acknowledges the need for improvement, he is not ready for corrective work. A good method of obtaining such a self-evaluation is by use of a tape recorder. The student reads while the teacher makes notes on which he will base his evaluation. The tape is analyzed and discussed in a friendly, constructive manner rather than in a critical way. This is a good starting procedure for a program of voice improvement. Where there is no tape recorder (and he should try to remedy the situation) the teacher's work is much harder and less satisfactory. He must draw the student's attention to specific components in his vocalization, hoping that the student will truly hear them for himself and not merely acquiesce in the teacher's judgment.

TYPICAL VOICE PROBLEMS

What voice problems do we find most often in our clinics that lend themselves to improvement? We shall reserve for later discussion problems of cleft-palate speech and organic nasality, and bypass entirely the problem of cerebral-palsied speech, which are two comparatively rare phenomena in regular public school clinics. The phenomena we find day in and day out are:

1. Breathiness
2. Inaudibility
3. Faulty pitch
4. Nasality
5. Lack of voice modulation
6. Monotone

7. Singsong pattern
8. Rising intonation and other types of foreign patterns
9. Harshness and stridency

Several of these voice faults, it will be seen — specifically, the first, second, sixth, and seventh — are directly related to the use of the voice in the melody pattern of speaking and reading. It is, therefore, wise to acquaint the student with the basic makeup of our melody pattern at the very start; namely, that there is an optimum pitch line that varies with the individual; that the thought-phrase is the unit in speaking and reading; that the voice is pitched highest on the first stressed syllable of the phrase; that it filters down to the pitch line in accordance with the length of the phrase; and, that a good half of one's adequacy in speaking will depend on understanding and mastering this last component.

VOICE AND THE OPTIMUM PITCH LINE

Where can we most effectively begin therapy? What will give us the most positive results for the limited time available? We suggest that there is more to be gained by building backward — that is, to present the concept of the line of intonation in the pitch range. Show the student how his flow of breath is related to his range, and where, exactly, he needs support.

For each of us there is a tone level, called variously optimum pitch, natural pitch, medium tone, to which our voice drops at the end of a unit of thought. Below this level we can lower our voice only a little, and that little generally sounds forced. Using the voice consistently above the optimum pitch, not permitting the tone to find its normal level, is both unnatural and strained. A speaker's range is the distance his voice travels between the top of his phrase and his optimum pitch. The high point has been observed by Klinghardt [1] to be the first stressed syllable of the

[1] Hermann Klinghardt, *Übungen in deutschem Tonfall. Für Lehrer und Studierende* (Leipzig, Verlag Von Quelle & Meyer, 1927).

phrase, the unstressed ones preceding it staying close to the OP line. It is the control of the material within that range, the playing out of the voice in accordance with the length of the phrase, the use of inflectional nuances, timing, and emphasis that make a competent speaker and reader. It is these techniques that the clinician teaches in challenging drills. Conversely, the student's failures in these areas need analysis and correction. We are of the opinion that more improvement can be obtained, more clarity, more carry-over, from corrective work of this kind than from any other aspect of our work.

Let the clinician therefore carefully appraise the voice and speech pattern of the student. What is it specifically that he does or does not do? Has he an adequate range? Does he, that is, jump his voice to a sufficiently high starting point? Does he adjust his steps in accordance with the length of the phrase? Or does he, conversely, immediately drop to his optimum pitch line? If so, his voice lacks support. Does he use his voice below his OP line, a tendency on the part of male adolescents during the period of their voice change, but observable also in others. These are the specifics that the clinician should check.

BREATHINESS

Is the voice breathy? If so, is it because the student mistakenly thinks that he hasn't enough breath? Squelch that thought immediately! If the voice is used properly in the range pattern, one needs only a minimal amount of breath, *i.e.*, support. What is probably happening is that he is bottling up his breath and releasing it without phonation. He then tries to speak on the remaining air. Let him observe himself critically. Does he tighten the muscles of his throat or upper chest? If so, it will interfere with the easy use of the breath and must, therefore, be eliminated. Does he try to speak on inspiration of the breath rather than expiration? Though not usual, such cases have been known to exist. Are there exercises to develop proper breath control? Chest expansion? Diaphragmatic breathing? Yes, there are useful exercises of this type, probably not especially needed by the average speaker, but certainly therapeutic for anyone. Let us be sure, however, that we know what we can and what we cannot do with these exercises.

If we tap our way about the chest frame, we should feel the following: the upper bones (sternum and clavicles) are hard and firm and move only slightly even on deep inspiration. The chest cage is formed of ribs that are attached to the sternum in front and to the backbone, except for the two bottom ribs, which are not attached at the front. Why, we ask, is this so? Let us put our hands on the ribs and breathe in several times — normally, and then deeply, holding the last breath and releasing it slowly. Can we describe what we feel under our hands? What part of the chest has nature prepared for breathing? Obviously it is in this lower region that the greatest expansion occurs. Now we know why the bottom ribs have been left free.

The chest and stomach cavities are separated by a bowllike muscle, concave side down, called the diaphragm. When we breathe, the muscle bundles that lie horizontally do the only thing muscles are able to do — they contract, that is, they get shorter. What does that do to the "bowl" of the diaphragm? Which cavity, chest or stomach, is thereby enlarged? Perhaps you have had occasion to watch a baby breathe and have noticed his belly go forward with his breathing. Does ours? We hope so, for in all this process of breathing just described, it is at one point only — namely, with the abdominal muscle — that we can consciously control the breathing process. The ribs, the intercostal muscles, and the diaphragm move automatically with the action of the abdominal muscle. If this muscle is pushed forward, the diaphragm is able to flatten and push downward, the floating ribs to move sideways and up, and the air to fill the lungs.

Some people may remember a film in which Jeanette Mac-Donald played the role of a hopeful singer being prepared for a career in opera by an irascible but top-notch voice coach. He starts her training by having her lie flat on her back and placing a volume of the *Encyclopaedia Britannica* on her stomach. This formidable volume has to be forced up and down by her breathing. But this is only the beginning. The set has twenty volumes, and before it is over, adding one volume at a time, she develops her stomach muscles until she can move all of the books.

Breathing, then, is in part a physical, muscular, manipulative process. It is also in part a chemically controlled automatic process. Functionally it underlies the movement of the voice in the intonation pattern. Therefore we must differentiate between these two functions and not confuse exercises for developing the physical structure with those for developing the breath control in the voice line. Voice control is obtained in speaking; muscle control in exercising. Development of voice control means the development of the voice range. And never tell a student that you are going to teach him to breathe "properly." All breathing is very proper indeed. Your best device for developing man's great glory of expression, the well-sustained tone, is to practice in graded phrases and selections, making quite sure that the pupils understand the principles of intonation involved.

THE INAUDIBLE VOICE

The pupil with an inaudible voice may be a frightened child; he may be defensively protecting himself from an over-insistent mother or sibling; he may be hiding the fact of voice change. A young girl may mistakenly consider it a more appealing or ladylike way of speaking. In all these instances there is, obviously, a psychological element. The student may have an aphonic voice for several purely physical reasons: laryngitis or pharyngitis, nodules, postnasal drip, or undeveloped voice. When the teacher is convinced that the psychological or physical elements are not the determining factors, he may help the student to become more audible by instructing him to:

- direct his eye contact to several distant parts of the room.
- project his voice in a parabola — that is, to think of it not as a straight line between him and a target receiver, but as a sound wave that is started upward on a curve.
- stress those elements of enunciation that will develop open tones, such as /ɑ/ /ɑʊ/ /æ/ /aɪ/.
- encourage frontal placement by using the front vowel sounds and front-articulated consonants.
- encourage his interest in communication.

THE UNMODULATED VOICE

Where the opposite fault is present, where the voice is too loud, it is well to ascertain first whether it is not due to a lingering but mistaken standard of excellence implanted in the lower grades. This is sometimes the case and needs perhaps only a word of comment to be overcome. Generally, students should be made aware that the very communication they are trying so hard to achieve is being balked by the overly loud voice. The receiver is alienated psychologically by the show of force. He is also repelled physically, his eardrums tiring from the bombardment of sound. The student should practice adjusting his voice to different spots, near and far, in the room. It may be that he has used one volume of voice for all his public utterances. His first contact with the idea of adjustment may be all he will ever need.

The unmodulated voice may also have an imitative base, a possibility the teacher may wish to explore. What is often true of this quality of voice is that it has limited flexibility, so that reading selections stressing change of tone, mood, rate, and emphasis are valuable drills. The clinician may want to discuss the question of proper consideration for the feelings of others. Lastly, the clinician must also be aware that the unmodulated voice may be an indication of hearing loss. Most likely, the unmodulated voice indicates a psychological rather than physical cause.

THE MONOTONE VOICE

The monotonous voice may or may not be a monotone, but a monotone is always monotonous to listen to — a generalization that in turn has to be qualified. There was a teacher who often enlivened our conferences with folksy stories. He was a fine narrator and master of the technique of building up to a climax. As his monotone voice filled in detail after detail, his eyes sparkled, and his rotund face looked as if it had just gobbled up a mouthful of smiles. His was not a monotonous monotone. Most monotones, however, are, and we, the listeners, are likely to wonder why the speaker's voice never "gets off the ground." Moreover, we begin to feel inadequate, as if we were not worth his effort to make the thought clear and interesting. The speech seems "flat." Here again, the teacher will first enlist the student's own understanding of what is happening, using, if available, a tape recorder, and then introducing him to the techniques of voice melody.

THE SINGSONG PATTERN

The use of a single, repeated, often foreign-sounding intonation pattern is called singsong. It predisposes the speaker to use phrases of approximately the same length. The melody pattern, too, is always the same. It appears unintelligent and unimaginative. For example, the singsong speaker would say:*

"I come to school . . ⌢and see his teacher. . . ⌢ and we make an agreement . . . . . ⌢ that if I control the television . . . . . . ⌢and check the homework . . . ⌢ he would report Ned's marks to me • • • •••.⌢every week •⌣ ."

To overcome this fault, the teacher uses a method, which may be summarized:

* Note marked circumflex glide.

listening to ⎫
listening for ⎬ the faulty pattern
hearing ⎭

listening to ⎫
listening for ⎬ the correct pattern
hearing ⎭

He should make a strong effort to enlist the student's full understanding and cooperation, remembering that in neighborhoods with large foreign-speaking populations a singsong pattern may represent the superimposed melody of the mother tongue.

A rising intonation is one type of foreign pattern, indicating, very often, a Yiddish influence. It reverses the melody line of English, leaving the thought suspended. A level intonation line rising at the end is typical of Spanish Americans. Here are some examples. Take sufficient time to be sure the student hears the fault.

	Correct	*Yiddish (Rising)*
You're coming to supper.		
I enjoy the study of English.		
What is the price of that garment?		

		Spanish
I am here with my family.		
I want to study English.		

NASALITY

Nonorganic nasality is a form of imbalance in resonance. The variety of forms of nasality are as many as the reasons that cause it. It is generally considered substandard and at the very least marring. It may arise equally from lax, inefficient organs of speech or from tight, strained, inflexible ones. It is often associated with specific mispronunciations; namely, ɛə / æ as in *man* and æʊ / ɑʊ as in *down* (shades of Eliza Doolittle!). When a student can be made to hear these mispronunciations and is willing to undertake the drills necessary for their correction, his problem can be solved comparatively easily.

There is also a form of functional nasality that grows out of a laxness of the soft palate and improper voice placement. Here it will be necessary to teach the student how to raise his palate and make it move more flexibly. The following is an exercise that can help the student overcome this problem:

> Pronounce a word ending in /ŋ/ such as *hang*. Hold the last sound, observing the position of the bulk of the tongue against the roof of the mouth. Now let the /ŋ/ die out, and gently pull the roof upward away from the tongue.
>
> Repeat, adding the sound *ah*. This will afford an open-throat pronunciation of the vowel. Retain this open-throat feeling and apply it to the chanting of phrases and lines of verse.

When the student is familiar with the sensation of the raised soft palate, drills like the following have meaning:

long (wrong, rang, sang of) evening, Easter holiday, illness, intake, effort, envelope, absence, act, island, idleness, overdue, omen, order, oar, arm, outcry, earth, urgent, onion, Anita

The
singer
wringer
hanger
bringer
swinger
stinger
} is going out.

The soft palate, moreover, may be induced to rise by physical drills like the following:

- With the mouth closed, take three short, sharp breaths on one inhalation, noting the successive positions of the soft palate. Maintain the last position for a moment. After some practice, the student should be able to raise the palate without the preliminary inhalation.
- The student should observe the movement of the soft palate in a hand mirror while panting vigorously. If done with sufficient vigor, he should see the soft palate rise and fall.
- For those who like the taste and don't mind the calories, a teaspoon of peanut butter, chewed and swallowed, will give the soft palate a good workout.
- An induced yawn simulates nature's way of relaxing the whole speech musculature and at the same time stretching the palate. Once the student can raise his palate at will, he should use it in that position to make clear vowel sounds.

The foregoing analysis of voice problems is by no means an exhaustive reference for the school clinician, but it presents the most common cases he may expect to find in his clinics and offers valid procedures for handling them.

SELECTIONS FOR PRACTICE

1. Note the necessary adaptation of the voice to the rising climax and the anticlimax:

> *King's cross!*
> *What shall we do?*
> *His royal robe*
> *Is rent in two!*
> *Out of his Crown*

He's torn the gems!
He's thrown his sceptre
Into the Thames!
The Court is shaking
In its shoes—
King's cross!
What *shall we do?*
Leave him alone
For a minute or two.
— ELEANOR FARJEON *

2. (Preferably for girls) Can you evoke the chiding quality of voice, spiced with flirtatiousness, that this passage suggests?

They're always abusing the women, as a terrible plague to men!
They say we're the root of all evil, and repeat it again and again;
Of war, and quarrels, and bloodshed, all mischief, be what it may!
And pray, then, why do you marry us, if we're all the plagues you say.
And why do you take such care of us, and keep us so safe at home,
And are never easy a moment if ever we chance to roam,
When you ought to be thanking heaven that your Plague is out of the
way
You all keep fussing and fretting — "Where is my Plague today?"
If a Plague peeps out of the window, up go the eyes of men;
If she hides, then they all keep staring until she looks out again.
— CAROLYN WELLS †

3. A selection for sustained mood. What phrases would the voice heighten? Can you suggest concomitant action?

After the laughter, after the light,
We came home through the wood tonight.
The wood beneath the naked sky
Seemed waiting for us to pass it by.
The green excitement of that wood
Hushed abruptly where we stood.

* "King's Cross" is reprinted from *Nursery Rhymes of London Town* by Eleanor Farjeon. Gerald Duckworth, Publisher. By permission of David Higham Associates, Ltd.
† "Chorus of Women" from *The Book of Humorous Verse* by Carolyn Wells. Reprinted by permission of Maurice O'Connell.

The rigid trees we stared upon
Seemed to wish the intruder gone.
We held our breaths, and our hearts beat hard
We quickened our steps, and the whole wood stared.
The trees seemed trying not to stare,
But we knew they wanted us out of there.
We felt that tall wood stiffen, stand tight,
As we came home through the trees tonight.
Like a single eye they followed our backs
Then turned, we felt the wood relax.
— JOSEPH AUSLANDER *

4. Modern poetry demands a strong emphatic pattern from the reader, the voice making decisive partitions of the thought.

On this wall, in this town, in their own state
We name their individual names, to state
That they were not just group, crew, squad, alone,
But each one man, one mortal self, alone,
Who fought the brutal frenzy of his time,
Who touched with human hand this iron time.
We give to them, who died in every weather,
Grief like an old wound groaning with the weather.
They knew death as a family dog knows men,
By whistle, touch, familiar smell of men,
But still were cheerful, still could ask each morning,
What do you know for sure on a new morning?
Before death's final stammer in the throat
Knew love's live stammer in the breathing throat.

       .   .   .   .   .

They flew to kill and some of them were killed.
They bombed the concrete fort and broke the city.
They turned their armed, trained face to the enemy.
Nothing is to be pitied here but pity.
They did their job and saved a state. Their skilled
Hands are shattered into history.
— PAUL ENGLE ‡
FROM "FOR THE IOWA DEAD"

QUESTIONS FOR DISCUSSION

1. Discuss the following statements. Do you agree or disagree with them?

   a. Your voice is you.

   b. "Her voice was always soft, gentle and low . . . an excellent thing in woman." — WILLIAM SHAKESPEARE, *King Lear*

   c. When one is depressed the voice tends to be dull; when one is happy it is lively and bright. Can you describe these qualities in physiological terms? Is there a parallel in body movement?

   d. Hitler's voice was effective and efficient. It would be equally so today.

2. Which of the following would you choose as narrator for a TV program on United States history? Why or why not?

   Marlon Brando, Robert Preston, Elizabeth Taylor, Sir Laurence Olivier, Lee Remick, Frank Sinatra, Geraldine Page, Elvis Presley, Richard Burton

3. Which of the following do you prefer as a speaker? Is your judgment objective?

   H. Rap Brown or Martin Luther King?
   Chet Huntley or David Brinkley?
   Alan Burke or Merv Griffin?
   President Nixon or Eugene McCarthy?
   Jacqueline Onassis or Barbra Streisand?
   Carol Burnett or Ingrid Bergman?
   Dean Martin or Bob Hope?

VI

The Stutterer's Clinic

———◆———

THEORY AND THERAPY

You have been assigned to direct a clinic of stutterers. No doubt you are apprehensive; undoubtedly enthusiastic. Here, you believe, is an area in which you can be maximally useful and achieve dramatic and deeply satisfying results. You expect to learn a great deal about your students; you arrange to take case histories; you aspire to establish an island of peace in a cluttered world. You are crammed full of theories — historical, medical, psychological. BUT, what do *YOU*, personally, really believe about stuttering? What results do you believe can be achieved? The therapy you introduce has a direct relation to the answers you give to these questions. Consider this also: You are a clinician and teacher, employed to conduct a group therapy program. You are not a doctor; you do not receive patients for individual consultation. If, for example, you believe fundamentally in the theory that stuttering is a "pregenital conversion neurosis amenable only

75

to therapy through psychoanalysis or psychotherapy"[1] we aver that you cannot be of definitive help to the group, since psychotherapy is not within your province in an educational setting. At the proper time, you may wish to make a referral for psychotherapy in an individual case.

There are a great number of theories and therapies that can be adapted to group clinical practice. Among them are: that there are multiple origins of the phenomenon of stuttering; that we have no basic etiology but only the statistics of clinical observation and research studies to guide us; that stuttering develops mainly in childhood; that it runs in families, especially those with left-handedness; that it is more prevalent in males; that it is associated with poor articulation, late speech development, muscular spasms; and that it is increased by fear.

You may recall that stuttering may be a temporary amnesia, or that the causal phenomenon has an "approach-avoidance base"; that it is a speech manifestation, or a product of interaction involving perceptive and evaluative reactions of listener and speaker; that it is an "anticipatory struggle reaction"; or you may think of it as a "non-fluency" in an environment that is intolerant of nonfluency.[2] (It is not our purpose within the limits of this discussion to include all of the many theories and explanations of stuttering. The teacher desiring further elucidation is referred to Eugene Hahn's *Stuttering: Significant Theories and Therapies*.)

Tracks and Truisms

While the experts indoctrinate, what should you as a clinician choose to do? Many theories have a place in the clinic and can form the basis of effective therapy. An eclectic approach, therefore, is not only wise but requisite. Not every stutterer has the same needs as every other one; not every stutterer responds to every approach. If the clinician remembers this, and then

[1] Jon Eisenson, ed., *Stuttering: A Symposium* (New York, Harper & Row, 1958), p. 78.
[2] Eisenson, *op. cit.*, pp. 125, 192, 4.

asks his students to try to understand that they may not respond to a particular approach, he may then discard, without further explanation, procedures that do not prove successful. The following, however, are truisms you cannot afford to neglect:

Accept what the student can do without stressing what he cannot. Encourage him to accept himself as he is, and to project himself as he expects to be. Be on the alert to help him recognize his improvement and positive achievement (stutterers tend to belittle anything short of complete fluency). Discuss with him aspects of his entire personality in such a way that he accepts the fact that his speech is only one facet of his relationship and communication with the world. Challenge him to set goals for himself that he can realistically achieve. Change these goals from time to time as his speech improves. For instance, he may at the beginning of the term "achieve" a moment's pause before addressing a given person or before reading to the group. Perhaps in a week or two he may be able to stabilize the use of key words or phrases in round robins or short presentations. Involve the students with each other, particularly in evaluating their successes and the reasons for their failure. And always encourage them to think less about themselves and more about others, and to learn to talk about and analyze their problems with therapeutic interest. We must recognize the fact that group therapy can give the stutterer an opportunity to share his feelings and to arrive at an understanding of his problem. He will then feel the need to do something about it. As each member of a group confronts himself and the group with his problem, and is, in turn, confronted by the others, motivation is reinforced. Analysis is mutual. The results achieved in group therapy are not always able to be realized through individual therapy.

PROCEDURES IN THE CLINIC

We have now established the point that the therapy we introduce into the clinic should have a direct relation to a theory we believe in or wish to try out. Below are some procedures, related to their theoretical matrix, that can be used in group therapy. It is important that the group understand that each drill, however simple it appears, is purposeful, and that success in relatively small, uncharged situations holds the key to developing parallel successes in situations offering more rigorous challenges. This is, in essence, the educational approach. It is inadequate for those needing medical supervision or psychotherapy, for example, the student who subconsciously clings to stuttering as a shield from responsibility. However, group therapy, as outlined above, is the service most schools are equipped to provide.

Some Recommended Therapies

1. SETTING THE PATTERN

Set a pattern of pause and intonation by group practice. For example, using the sequence / "My name is ——. What's yours?" / introduce variations in accordance with the general interests and sophistication of the group:

"I live at ——. And you?"
"My favorite subject is ——. What's yours?"
"*My Three Sons* is a delightful TV comedy. What is your TV favorite?"
"My hobby is ——. Have you one?"
"If I could vote, I'd vote for ——. And you?"

Such practice lends itself to a chain technique. Start with the first student, who turns and passes the phrase to the next, and so on around the group until the last one is reached. This one then "ties" the chain by passing the phrase to the initiator. The value of a chain drill on pattern phrases is that it minimizes recall and is a good starting point for the group. It is sound practice, too, in that it involves speech directed to a listener. Early group drills must allow the student to feel successful.

2. LEARNED RELAXATION

Discuss physical manifestations of fear with your students, eliciting from each how fear expresses itself in his individual case and in others he may have observed. Explain that there is a form of relaxation that can be learned.[3] By studying our muscles when they are tight and when they are relaxed we acquire a memory of relaxed muscle tonus. We can then use this remembered feeling in some measure to control our fear manifestation in a real situation. Using this technique, conduct a drill for the relaxation of the hand:

> Make a tight fist . . . tighter . . . tighter. Do you feel the tightness? Now begin to relax your hand very slowly . . . a little at a time. A bit more . . . and more . . . and more. Observe the position of the hand. Are the fingers stretched out? No, of course not. That would not be true relaxation. How did your hand muscles feel when you were relaxing them? Can you remember that feeling? Now tighten your hand *just a bit* and then relax it. Relax it without preliminary tightening. Was there tension there?

Plan a unit of therapy, applying the drill to arms and shoulders, legs and feet, head, face muscles, and finally, control of the stomach muscles. No more than ten minutes should be projected for each session in the beginning. You may need more time when it is combined with breath control. Subsequently, you may wish to revert to a short refresher.

3. RATE-CONTROL TECHNIQUE

Many stutterers, particularly those with marked blocks, have profited from this technique, which builds up from syllable to word to phrase. The clinician explains the technique,[4] placing a couplet or quatrain on the blackboard. Cooperatively with the group, he decides on the pauses in the selection (breath groups)

---

[3] Edward Jacobson, *Progressive Relaxation* (Chicago, University of Chicago Press, 1951).
[4] James F. Bender and Victor M. Kleinfeld, *Speech Correction Manual* (New York, Farrar & Rinehart, 1937), pp. 195–198.

and marks them. He establishes a beat, one per syllable, counting a double beat for pauses and a double beat to begin — "Two for nothing." He must be sure, however, that the students understand that this method entails their *following* a beat. It is entirely out of the question for them to initiate their own beat. In the first instance, they adapt themselves and develop control; in the second they would be using a crutch. The clinician keeps the beat with a dull thud. A pencil or ruler will do this very well. At the beginning it is often better to call out "one-two" for pauses before the group starts. Now let the group intone, watching for pauses and entering on a beat. At this level the desired result is an unbroken chant within the phrase, and open-mouth vowels. The use of a monotone is likely to occur but should be discouraged. This is Step 1. For example: [Each dot represents a beat]

. . . .

The day is done, | and the darkness

. . . . . .

Falls | from the wings of Night,

. . . .

As a feather is wafted downward

. . . . . .

From an eagle in his flight.
— HENRY WADSWORTH LONGFELLOW
"THE DAY IS DONE"

In Step 2, decide, cooperatively, on the stressed words and mark them. Determine the beat, this time one per stress, keeping the introductory beats and the beats for pauses. Repeat the selection in this pattern, the objective being the use of the voice in emphasis, that is, an inflectional pattern. The result at this point more closely resembles normal speech. Example:

$$\overset{\bullet}{The}\ \overset{\bullet}{day}\ is\ \overset{\bullet}{done},\ |\ and\ the\ darkness$$

The day is done, | and the darkness

Falls | from the wings of Night |

As a feather is wafted downward |

From an eagle in its flight. ||

Step 3 approximates Step 2 in that it keeps the pauses and stress pattern, but does not use a beat. In a small group it is desirable to have each student repeat the selection alone, choosing the level (Step 1, 2, or 3) where he feels he can function best at the moment. It is part of the clinician's obligation to minimize failure in this drill while keeping rigorously to its demands. A student who understands that he is more successful when he chooses realistically the level at which he can read than if he forces himself beyond his present hope of achievement is already launched on the path of improvement. The feeling of euphoria created by the predictable success in this drill provides great encouragement for the group as well as for the individual.

Set up a unit of therapy employing this technique, using a variety of selections of varying degrees of difficulty: prose, conversation, selections of emotional import such as speeches of rebellion and of conflict between parents and children, young and old, and selections from plays. Develop appreciation for phrasing and stressing and permit individual students to "prepare the selection," i.e., indicate the pauses and stresses, at the board. The grouping of words in thought units and the voice patterns within them, and the pattern of pauses between phrases, the sustaining ability of the voice, the manipulative devices of inflection will gradually transfer — hopefully — to the students' free speech. A not-very-bright student developed a considerable knack for indicating phrase and stress at the board. He was justly proud of his ability and was encouraged to be so. Although his own speech often faltered, he had a sense of direction and achievement. It is unfortunate, as the profession knows,[5] that public education rarely provides a follow-up service for these students after they leave the school.

4. CHEWING THERAPY

"Chewing is the origin of human speech." One of the therapies that has proved to be helpful in modifying and overcoming stuttering is the chewing approach as advanced originally by Froeschels and later by his disciples, Weiss, Beebe, Mohr and others.[6]

Because it is based on a sound physiological principle, it is easy to explain and to illustrate. It is almost always effective from the beginning not only with individuals but with small groups. The success of the therapy depends upon a careful explanation and presentation by the clinician. His first goal is to change the student's concept of his speech as an activity consisting of "difficult and easy" sounds and words, to one that can be produced naturally and without effort.

- Explain that speaking and chewing are identical processes; that the same mechanism and the same sets of muscles are involved in the production of fluent sounds in speaking and chewing; that the movements of the jaw and tongue and

[5] Dorothy Doob, "What Constitutes Success in Therapy for Stutterers" (Paper delivered at the Speech Association of America Conference, Chicago, December, 1966).
[6] Deso A. Weiss and Helen H. Beebe, eds., *The Chewing Approach in Voice and Speech Therapy* (Basel and New York, S. Karger, 1959).

the regulation of the breath that occur in chewing include all the activity required for the production of sounds for spoken language.

• State that chewing is a continuous act, as is the emission of words; that the kinesthesia of talking and chewing, therefore, have much in common.

In applying the technique, the student is first asked to chew with his mouth wide open. He must produce vigorous chewing movements, e.g., audible smacking of lips, tongue activity, etc. A mirror often helps him to visualize this activity. He is then asked to chew using voice, producing a variety of nonsense sounds. If the chewing appears to be produced mechanically, the clinician must immediately interrupt and demonstrate a correct vigorous "chew" of sound. This is most important to establish at the very beginning of therapy. The student must be encouraged to use all the organs of articulation in chewing.

At this point, as the student begins the therapy and watches himself, in the mirror, making facial grimaces and rather awkward movements of the lips and jaw, in addition to producing unintelligible sounds, he may very well say that it all seems "funny" or "extremely impolite." The clinician explains that, for the moment, he can forget Emily Post, and that the success of the therapy depends on this initial vigor. Continue the chewing of nonsense sounds for several minutes only, as the unaccustomed use of the muscles in the oral area may become physically exhausting. If the student is unable to establish correct chewing after several attempts, he may be helped by the use of gumdrops, marshmallows, or chewing gum. Once the correct chewing of sounds has been mastered, it can be applied in the following ways:

• The clinician and student begin to chew alternately, first a few syllables at a time, keeping up a conversation in nonsense sounds:

a why oh me loo
tee low tah may lee
ba boh lee too moh
wah low koo knee eye

- The student then intersperses his nonsense chewing with a
few words of spoken chewed language:

Pah lay? ka bee *will do* ah no *if you* see no flay too.

From this point, if he successfully achieves fluent chewing
of a few words, without any break in rhythm, he may proceed to
short sentences, poems, and prose. At first these should be preceded by a nonsense chew and chewing sounds interspersed
within the phrase:

Ee-oh-ay *I pledge allegiance* nee-naw-pay *to the flag* oy-soy
bun-say *of the United States of America,* and so on.

As the individual progresses, and no longer needs help to get the
feel of a chew, you will note that real patterns of fluency become
established. You will note, too, that therapy has become an interaction process involving an exchange between clinician and student.

The last and most difficult part of the therapy is the carry-
over to free conversation. The student should be asked to continue vigorous chewing at home at least ten to twenty times a
day for short periods of time to be certain that he establishes the
technique firmly. Gradually, he will make less vigorous movements and transfer the physical technique to the "thinking" of it,
so that it will no longer be so obvious. Although this is just another approach to the many-faceted problem of stuttering, it has
produced successful results. In addition, the student always has
a technique to return to in the event that he lapses into nonfluent
speech. Remember, it is impossible to stutter if you are able to
chew sound!

5. NEGATIVE PRACTICE

As we have indicated, there are many therapeutic approaches for the stutterer. He will be introduced to blendings, patterns, breathing rituals, rate-controlled speech, pitch variations, breath chewing and other variations of the speaking process.

It is Bryngelson [7] who developed the therapeutic concept of voluntary or intentional stuttering, which is the approach known as "negative practice." This technique requires the stutterer to deliberately and voluntarily practice the errors he has been making involuntarily and unintentionally. The purpose of this is to help the student break habits that have become fixed and automatic. He must control the habit that has controlled him.

The stutterer is instructed to repeat his complete spasm and stutter intentionally. He should also be directed to try to make himself feel the way he does during his involuntary stuttering. He will not succeed in reproducing this feeling, nor is he likely to succeed in the complete reproduction of an involuntary spasm. But he must try! He may observe himself in a mirror; he may try to imitate how he sounds by listening to a tape recording of his speech. When he becomes efficient at self-imitation, the stutterer is ready for his next step in voluntary stuttering. He begins by repeating his evocation, modifying it in one or more aspects decided on in advance. He may decide that he will repeat the initial sound twice, or prolong the initial sounds, or speak at a slower or faster rate. Normal fluent speech is not the immediate goal; rather, it is the control of stuttering through modified stuttering. Even if the individual feels that he can speak without stuttering he must pretend or "fake stutter" — but in a manner different from his usual way of stuttering. After he does it differently, the stutterer is further directed to stutter easily, without struggle behavior, without blocks, progressing and repeating, if necessary, with lessened tension and without "backing-up." The objective at this stage of therapy — which it is important that the

---

[7] Eisenson, *op. cit.*, p. 261.

stutterer understand — is to weaken his own stuttering pattern and to substitute for it a more fluent form of stuttering. Van Riper [8] details some of the techniques of this therapy, which he terms "cancellation techniques."

This approach is especially recommended for group therapy. If the voluntary stuttering proves too difficult under these conditions, it is suggested that the stutterer be taught to permit the symptoms to appear openly without attempting to avoid or inhibit them. Willingness to stutter openly is a goal of this type of therapy. Progressive improvement — the goal of the educational approach — should be expected, until, in time, the control over speech is natural.

6. SPEECH DIARY AND EVALUATION

Direct each student to keep a simple diary for one day, noting all occasions on which he spoke and commenting on his successes, failures, and on the particular circumstances. Have the student devise a schematic plan or use anecdotal entries. Have him indicate the class periods, including lunch, pre- and post-school time, and make note of the speech activities of the day — at work, at play, and in recitation, in conversation with the family, with peers, special oral reports in classes, responses to questions, requests for information and failures to respond. This record serves many purposes: [9]

- It is interesting for the student to report on. It involves self-confrontation.
- It is important for the student to evaluate himself, and especially valuable for him to note small successes, which he tends to bypass.

[8] Charles Van Riper, *Speech Correction* (Englewood Cliffs, N.J., Prentice-Hall, 1963), p. 405.
[9] Loosely adapted from theories in Wendell Johnson, *et al.*, *Speech Handicapped School Children.* No clinician should presume to conduct a speech clinic without having read Johnson's chapter on stuttering. It is a most valid presentation of theory on the subject.

- It is valuable to others in the group to make comparisons.
- It provides the teacher with useful insights.
- It furnishes a tangible record, over a period of time, of specific nodes of improvement and/or problems.
- It provides good material for free conversation.

Reproduced below is one such card using anecdotal entries:

Name _____ Date _____ Clinic _____

SPEECH DIARY

Place	Entry
B'kfast	Asked for money — felt funny — allowance day is Sat. ST a lot. Pop gave it to me right away but didn't say anything. I talked a lot myself.
To skl.	Walked with a girl I know. Never ST.
Per 1	History. I like it. We got into a real fight on slavery. Wanted to say something but was all tied up.
Per 2	English. Hate it, esp. grammar. Didn't say anything.
Per 3	French. Gen'lly good but was unprepared. Teacher doesn't call on me when I say I can't talk. Lucky.
Lunch	Wish we were co-ed. Snuck over and talked to Emma.
Per 5	Math. Explained proposition at board. Felt good.
" 6	Music. Listened to record and sang. Teacher said I was a baritone.
H.E.	Best period of the day. Practiced sinking baskets. Guess I hollered like everyone else.
Service	Audio-Visual lab. Mr. P. is one swell guy. No biz so we talked about what it costs to go to college. ST a little, but he doesn't care.
Street	Stickball — Boynton vs. Elder. We won. Got into argument which I hate.
Evening	Nothing much. Homework. TV. Pop asked, "What do you need so much money for?" I said, "Try living on $2 a week today."

It would be condescending for us to analyze each point in this record; a few will suffice to show significant factors:

- The relation between anticipated unpleasantness and accelerated nonfluency.

- The nonorganic nature of the phenomenon: it tends to appear and disappear.
- The relation between unpreparedness and poor recitations. Why should the stutterer have special dispensation in the matter of preparation?
- What is the stutterer's speaking obligation in his classes?
- The effect on the stutterer of the personality of his teachers.
- Emotional hang-ups. Relationships of the stutterer to his peers.

In the classroom the completed cards will be used for reports, cross-questioning, and group discussion. Effort should be made to keep the atmosphere of such discussion light, interesting, and cooperative. Elicit comparable experiences. Repeat the assignment at intervals of one or two weeks.

7. SIMPLE DISCUSSION: TECHNIQUE

Free discussion is much appreciated in this group when introduced later in the term. One may use, for instance, a series of situations dominated by the question "Was it justified?"

Steve is a new driver who was stopped on the parkway when the traffic was comparatively light. The policeman ticketed him for going 52 miles an hour in a 45-mile zone. *Was it justified?*

The following week Steve was again stopped. The policeman said, looking at his license, "A speeder, huh? I'll see that you learn your lesson this time." Steve claims that he was not going above the speed limit. *Was it justified?*

Mr. Katz, the butcher, gave Mrs. Gold too much change, which she decided to keep, thinking, "This will make up for the times he short-weighted me." *Was she justified?*

"Redeposit the ten cents," said the operator. Fifty cents dropped into the return box. He redeposited only ten cents. *Was he justified?*

It is readily seen that when students become familiar with this form of discussion, they can initiate discussion situations out of their own experience.

8. PARTIAL PATTERNS

Drills involving partial patterns are sophisticated and valuable devices using material partly set-up by the clinician and partly original with the stutterer. Group practice of the pattern precedes the round robin, the group noting the elements of phrasing and intonation that seem pertinent. The following examples will suggest some of the many forms the patterns can take:

- Begin a sentence with a phrase involving a date: *"In 1492,* Columbus discovered America." The students then substitute similarly structured sentences of their own, having "set" the pattern of the model with the group: *e.g., "In 1942,* I was born." *"In the year 1968,* Robert Kennedy was assassinated."

- Continue, using a variety of set phrases requiring completion by the students. The key phrase, "set" in the group, serves as the model and is always included:

  "When I play ball . . ."
  "Whenever I go shopping . . ."
  "My mother really expects me to . . ."
  "Books are like windows because . . ."
  "A code of ethics for students should require . . ."
  "Aha," said the ghost, "it's not me you're afraid of but . . ."
  "I have to take care of my two brothers because . . ."

- Use pairs of contrastive words, noting the inflectional pattern. Change the emotional tone of the second part when speaking, noting changes in the inflectional pattern and rate:

"First . . . , and then . . ."
"Once . . . , but now . . ."
"Some teachers . . . , while others . . ."
"Either do this . . . , or . . ."
"Males . . . , but females . . ."

9. CHORAL READING

Choral reading techniques are recommended and justified for use in the stutterers' clinic for exactly the same reasons as they would be for any class. They build language appreciation by reinforcing the sense of rhythm, by refining concepts of sound, by forcing modulations of the voice, by using a battery of interpretive techniques. They create orchestral effects possible only in group or unison reading, and provide challenges to the individual through solo reading. In the case of the stutterer it has the added advantage of helping him lose his self-consciousness because he is participating with the group. He does not feel that he stands out alone, and he also realizes that he is experiencing a sense of fluency in his speech.

The Clinic as Clearing House

The above suggestions are not methodology, but represent approaches used in providing students with opportunities for speaking, for analyzing speech patterns, for relating to and communicating with the group, for building confidence in themselves as speakers, and for learning to minimize their fear of speaking. In addition, the speech clinic should be a clearing house to which the stutterer may bring situations for analysis, analyze his frustrations in speech, and consider ways of building resistance to such frustrations.

Since a stutterer may very well continue in a clinic for a number of terms — some claim that it "gives me confidence" to attend — it is necessary that the clinician keep a careful record for each student. The record keeping is best done as soon as possible after meeting the clinic although sparse notes may be taken during the sessions. This should be recognized by the administration as an integral part of the work of the clinic and time be allotted for it.

Whatever activity is introduced into the stutterers' clinic, however, must be motivated on your part, by your belief in what it can do for the stutterer. There is a wealth of writing, theorizing, and experimentation on the subject which you must sift through for yourself to find what things you really believe in. Then, and only then, can you formulate your therapy and initiate educationally sound practices.

FURTHER ORIENTATION OF THE CLINICIAN

The clinician working with stutterers has it in his power to do considerable good if he does not confine his work to the clinic. A large part of his responsibility is to set in motion out-of-clinic activities and attitudes. Parents, guidance personnel, teachers, and athletic coaches can all play a role in the stutterer's program of conscious self-improvement. Parents, in the majority of cases, are only too anxious to cooperate and should be the first to be contacted. In conference with them the clinician will seek to familiarize himself with the student's background and to spot areas of tension such as:

* a teen-age boy who shares a bedroom with a sister
* a mediocre student who tries to satisfy his parents' unrealistic goals of excellence
* a stutterer who feels he must be a lawyer, etc., "like his father"
* an older sister burdened with the complete care of a younger sibling after school

Parents, moreover, often look to the teacher for practical guidance for themselves. The following suggestions, taken from an article by Dr. Francis Griffith,[10] are eminently practical.

PRACTICAL SUGGESTIONS TO PARENTS

1. See that he gets plenty of wholesome food and sufficient exercises. Games and exercises involving rhythms, such as skating, dancing, swimming, skipping rope and the like, are especially helpful. Because of emotional strain, stutterers tend to become fatigued more quickly than normal speakers. Hence adequate rest is essential. Remediable physical handicaps, such as diseased tonsils or teeth and defective eyesight, should get medical attention.

2. Maintain an atmosphere of ease and relaxation in the home. As far as possible keep the stutterer away from situations which excite and overstimulate. A congenial and pleasant home life created by a family in which all members love and help one another will be a major curative influence in the life of the speech-handicapped child.

3. Avoid making him overconscious of his speech. This is especially applicable to the young child.

4. Encourage him whenever you can. Discriminating praise helps build self-respect.

5. Teach him to be self-reliant. Avoid coddling.

6. Do not reprimand him for stuttering, mimic his stutter, or subject him to sarcasm.

7. Treat him as a normal person at all times. Do not let him use his stutter to escape obligations or obtain attention.

8. As far as possible use only one language at home. Bilingual conversation may aggravate his difficulty.

9. Encourage your child to participate in group activities with children of his own age and both sexes. Participation in games, parties, clubs and other such activities will facilitate his speech rehabilitation.

[10] Francis Griffith, "Does Your Child Stutter," *Hygeia* (now *Today's Health,* published by the American Medical Association), October, 1948. Reprinted by permission.

10. If your child is enrolled in a speech clinic, visit his teacher and find out how you can supplement his clinical procedures.

The speech clinician should help the student establish a favorable rapport with his teachers by stating his problems to them and defining, mutually, the limits of his oral participation, the purpose being not to evade work, but to provide the stutterer with a situation in which he can function realistically. He will then feel an obligation to meet his commitments as far as he can. He should understand that he will be living in a healthier atmosphere if he acknowledges his stuttering openly. He should not regard each incident of stuttering as a new failure but as an opportunity to function and to improve. A student may feel that he can handle short blackboard explanations but not prolonged discussion, that he can prepare himself for a book report, but cannot manage the give and take of a question period. He should be encouraged to find supplementary forms of participation such as doing outside research or bringing in illustrative material. He should be instructed how to relieve the tension inherent in a classroom presentation by varying direct speech with:

- Blackboard highlighting of the topic he is discussing, such as lists of characters or dates, etc. This will take his attention away from his own speech problem.
- Varying the narrative approach by turning the information into a series of questions.
- If he reads better than he speaks, let him begin by reading a pertinent quotation.
- Introduce visual material (pictures, etc.) which can be manipulated.

Under no circumstances should he use his stutter as an excuse for not participating, however small that participation may be. The following form for distribution to teachers can be used in this connection:

SPEECH CLINIC FOLLOW-UP

Dear _____,   Date _____

_____ a student in your _____ class is

a stutterer and attends speech clinic _____ on _____.

In order to assist this student in overcoming his difficulty, may we suggest that in your classroom meetings with him you observe the following procedures:

1. Call on him as frequently as you call on your other students, but, until he has learned to relax in your class, allow him to answer briefly.

2. Urge him to answer in sentence form as students should, but do not insist on this if he is unable to do so.

3. Do not supply words or hurry his responses.

4. Create an attitude of understanding on the part of his classmates without making him conspicuous. Treat his stutter matter-of-factly and do not stress it.

5. Kindly inform me of outstanding success or failure on his part so that we can make use of it in therapy.

If you would like to discuss this student's speech problem, get in touch with me.

Clinician, Speech Department

Approved.
Chairman, Speech Department

SCHOOLWIDE APPROACH

Promoting schoolwide understanding of the problem of stuttering is part of the speech clinician's obligation. He fulfills this by keeping himself available to the staff for advice and consultation on stuttering and stutterers. In addition, a faculty conference devoted to the subject of stuttering can be interesting and valuable. The statistics and numerous therapeutic approaches which are well-known to the clinician are generally unknown to the school faculty. Choose information that will give teachers greater insight in working with these students. The following are some of the concepts of stuttering that have been established, through research, as axiomatic.

- Stuttering is not a defect of speech. There is no correlation between it and mentality, or, if any, the scales are tipped in favor of those of higher ability.[11]
- It has been defined by a leading authority [12] as an anxiety reaction that has become frozen into behavior. While this is an excellent and educationally useful definition, there are others.
- Its incidence is estimated as one percent of the population. Among stutterers, however, boys outnumber girls four to one. (Some claim the proportion is higher.) The rate is higher for Negroes.
- At the high school level we rarely see primary stutterers. They have advanced to the secondary stage, where their avoidance techniques are what we are most conscious of.
- There is no single cause for stuttering. Causes that have been promulgated and have stood the test of time and/or scientific verification include:

  HANDEDNESS: There is no superiority of one type of dominance over another, and no onus, as witness "southpaws" in baseball. There is some discomfort which is even now being eliminated with specially constructed desks, etc. In those cases where it has been causal, it became so because of the conflict set up by a senseless change from what was natural and easy to a conformity that didn't fit.

  IMITATION: a possible but not probable cause. If this were really causal, the incidence would be much greater.

[11] It was found to be prevalent among British men of genius.
[12] Wendell Johnson, *Speech Handicapped School Children* (New York, Harper & Row, 1967), pp. 240–241.

HEREDITY: There is a strong hereditary influence, not so much as to physical or physiological functioning, but in nervous, sensitive tendencies, and in the background provided by parents who are at odds with their speech world.

ORGANIC ORIGIN: Quackery has nowhere been more repugnant than in the history of the treatment of stuttering. Operations were performed on organs that any doctor should have seen were not defective. How could they be when the stutterer could speak perfectly well some of the time? This does not preclude consideration of biochemical and neurological origins.

PSYCHOANALYSIS AND PSYCHOTHERAPY have not been as successful in dealing with it as with other psychoneuroses. Educational methods and therapy have certain great advantages, not the least of which is that they offer help at the place where it is needed.

Stutterers do improve under proper supervision. Not all improve equally or at the same rate. We have known a stutterer who made the valedictory address at his graduation. We were on the stage, and when he stopped in the middle of his speech, we found it impossible to breathe. Not so he. It was a calculated pause, and he picked up the thread of his discourse without any loss of confidence. If what we are doing is educationally sound, if we have made full use of our resources and resourcefulness, we should accept the measure of improvement the place, the time, and the person are capable of producing.

A LAST WORD TO THE CLINICIAN

The stutterer assigned to your class may have a clinical history both in and out of school. It is your responsibility to familiarize yourself with it as quickly as possible. You are the hub of his improvement program but there are many other spokes to the wheel: his parents or guardians, his guidance counselor, his health adviser, and his teachers are all to be consulted and subsequently advised by you. Although highly desirable, team procedures have not yet been made workable in schools. Services are limited. You can and should, however, discuss the problems of these students with your chairman or supervisor. In certain recognizable cases, the stutterer can be referred for a psychological work-up, which you, the clinician, can then use for insight into his speech problem. It is not a dream — you can be maximally useful and achieve deeply satisfying results.

VII
Clinic for Substandard Speech: Vowels

It is poor pedagogy to say that we are going to teach a child or teen-ager a sound. If, to our trained ear, he mispronounces the sound, or even if he lacks it entirely, his substitute for it adequately represents the sound for him. What you can do is to teach him *discrimination* between sounds. That is, train his ear, train his judgment. For this purpose, your thorough grounding in phonetics is your standby equipment. Every piece of it can be used for a worthwhile presentation if the particular clinic group can absorb it or profit from it. It is for this reason that we will survey the sounds of the language, stressing those aspects of their production that have most bearing on the correction of substandard or poorly articulated speech. We use broad transcription of the General American (GA) vowel scale with this modification.

Vowel mispronunciations often come from a confusion between similar sounds, *i.e.*, sounds close to one another on the vowel scales. Touching on the forms and causes of substitutions and malformations, our discussion will also suggest methods for elimi-

THE VOWEL SCALES

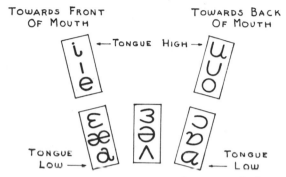

nating the most commonly encountered points of phonemic confusion.

THE FRONT VOWELS

These are so named because the front of the tongue is the tensed part and forms a hump toward the hard palate. It is important that students understand not only the diagrammatic value of the vowel chart, but the significance of the technical terms used. Suggest to them that they pronounce /i/ and /u/ in quick succession and note the movement and resting position of the tongue for each sound. They will observe that the /i/ is formed in the front of the mouth, the /u/ in the back. The tongue positions are:

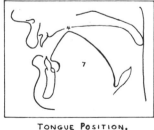

TONGUE POSITION,
FRONT VOWELS

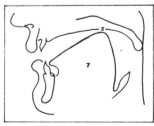

TONGUE POSITION,
BACK VOWELS

The vowels of the front scale to be considered are:

i ɪ e (eɪ) ɛ æ a (aɪ)

⎢ i/ɪ ⎢ The first two phonemes of the front vowel scale are often confused. In the high position we find a substitution of /ɪ/ for /i/ and vice versa. The result is a foreignism. Thus we hear "sit down on the seat" as sit dɑun ɒn ðə sɪt. To non-native speakers of Germanic or Spanish extraction the difference between these two sounds seems slight or nonexistent. These students must receive a barrage of stimuli to enable them to make the distinction a part of their automatic recognition. The following drills are postulated on the use of monitored tapes and recorders, but they can be used without them if each student has a copy of the exercises.

DRILL I: Listen for the sound of /i/ at the beginning of the word. Listen and repeat. Then listen and compare.

Edith, eater, eke, eel, even, eon, equal, Erie, Easter, each, either, eve, eat, easy, eerie *

DRILL II: Listen for the sound of /i/ in the accented syllable. Listen and repeat. Then listen and compare.

peep, peas, beak, bees, weak, weal, meek, meal, feet, feel, Veep, veal, thee, these, teak, team, deep, deem, leak, liege, reek, ream, neat, need, seat, seed, Zeke, zeal, sheik, she'll, cheek, cheese, Jeanie, jeans, keep, keel, queasy, geese, priest, preen, pleat, please, brief, breeze, bleak, bleed, fleece, fleas, freak, freed, three, treat, jeep, redeem, impede, repeat.

DRILL III: Twenty words will be read to you. If the word contains the sound of /i/ check it on the list provided; if not, leave it blank. Each word will be spoken twice.

* Note that the accent falls on the /i/

100

CLINIC FOR SUBSTANDARD SPEECH: VOWELS

1. teasing _____	11. price _____
2. teething _____	12. picture _____
3. tipping _____	13. piece _____
4. tide _____	14. string beans _____
5. illness _____	15. silly _____
6. infinity _____	16. remedial _____
7. measles _____	17. cheap _____
8. miserable _____	18. chip _____
9. simple _____	19. chili _____
10. season _____	20. feed _____

DRILL IV: Listen to the word pairs. Listen and repeat. Listen and compare.

peat – pit;   beat – bit;   meet – mitt;   wheat – wit;   feet – fit; veal – vigor; theory – thin; thee – this; team – Tim; deep – dip; least – list;   real – rill;   neat – knit;   seat – sit;   zero – zip; sheen – shin;   cheek – chin;   Jean – gin;   keel – kill;   he – his; Preem – prim;   breed – brig;   fleet – flit;   treacle – trickle; greet – grit

⎡ ɪ/e ⎤ The second and third vowels, /ɪ/ and /e/, are not often confused, the most prevalent error being a too open-mouthed pronunciation of the /e/. It should be noted that the first three vowels of the front and back scales are all pronounced with the tongue high in the mouth, and that the first real relaxation comes between the /e/ and the /ɛ/. (This is similarly the case between the back vowels /o/ and /ɔ/.) Several advertisements have cleverly exploited the difference between a sloppy and a pure pronunciation of the /e/. "Luckies taste better" will be remembered as one. In order to draw attention to the difference in the positioning of the /ɪ/ and /e/ it is necessary to practice them alone and in comparison with each other.

DRILL I: Listen to the sound of /ɪ/ at the beginning of the word. Listen and repeat. Then listen and compare.

101

imp, image, imbecile, Ibsen, ethereal, it, idiot, idiom, inn, ill, Iliad, is, issue, illustrate, itch, irritate, inch, incense, incident, indigo, Indo-China, inebriate, ineligible, indigent, inference, infinite, ingot, injury, inherit, igloo, ignorant, Icarus, inoculate, innocence, inquest, insolvent, inside, instant, interest, Isobel

DRILL II: Listen for the sound of /ɪ/ in the accented syllable. Listen and repeat. Then listen and compare.

will, Williams, whist, whimper, willow, widow, wisdom, wicked, winter, wish, which, wig, whip, will, mist, mint, million, misery, mission, Mitchell, miracle, mimicry, middle, mitten, minute, pill, pistol, pimple, pillow, pick, pippin, pickle, pinpoint, pitch, bill, blister, blimp, billow, abysmal, bin, bicker, bid, bit, fill, filter, fist, fizz, fickle, fish, fib, fiddle, fin, filch, flicker, fill, filter, fiscal, figure, fiction, filament, finger, village, vintage, victory, vicar, victuals, villain, vinegar, vindicate, virile, visage, vision, Vivian, vivid, thrill, thistle, thing, thick, thicket, thin, thimble, think, thither, this, till, twist, Timothy, tinker, tick, tickle, ticket, tin, ticker, tint, twitch, tissue, tip, tidbit, timber, tinsel, dill, distance, dint, dimple, dicker, dish, ditch, dig, dip, did, Disneyland, different, dribble, digit, dignity, diplomat, dividend, Lillian, list, listen, limp, lick, Litchfield, linnet, licorice, liberal, lid, lip, ligament, limit, literate, lizard, liver, livable, rill, wrist, rich, river, risen, rim, rib, rip, rig, rift, risk, ribbon, ridge, rigid, rivet, sill, silly, sip, simple, sibilant, sympathy, sit, stitch, swim, swift, still, sin, stint, sing, single, spin, splint, skin, skinflint, silk, sick, sickle, sieve, sift, stigma, signal, signify, silver, simmer, since, sister, syrup, skill, shrill, ship, shibboleth, shingle, shimmer, shift, shiver, chill, chicory, chick, chimney, chip, Jill, Jim, gibbet, gist, gypsy, jig, jigger, jiffy, jitters, kill, kindle, kissed, king, click, kick, Kim, kid, kidney, kindergarten, kipper, kinky, kitchen, kin, kitten, guilty, giddy, gift, guild, give, diminish, insist, Elizabeth, belligerent, invisible, militant

DRILL III: Twenty words will be read to you. If the word contains the sound of /ɪ/ check it on the list provided; if not, leave it blank. Each word will be spoken twice.

1. tepee _____
2. wigwam _____
3. steal _____
4. sieve _____
5. interest _____
6. winter _____
7. sprint _____
8. evil _____
9. enter _____
10. Istanbul _____

11. single _____
12. Benito _____
13. benediction _____
14. thrill _____
15. implement _____
16. tent _____
17. tint _____
18. team _____
19. mind _____
20. mineral _____

A word of caution. The student should think of these drills as a combination of ear and muscle training. It is sufficient for the clinician to state that all words are in good English usage and that their meaning is of no immediate concern. A few minutes reserved at the end of the drill for a pick-and-choose discussion of several of the more useful words is a satisfactory procedure.

DRILL I: Listen to the sound of /e/ at the beginning of the word. Listen and repeat. Then listen and compare.

epic, episode, ebb, ebony, eminent, M.D., effort, effigy, ever, evidence, ethical, Ethel, etiquette, etcetera, Eddie, edit, enemy, enter, Esther, essay (n), Ezra, echelon, etch, edge, error, element, elephant, equitable, excellent, egg, examine

103

DRILL II: Listen to the sound of /e/ in the accented syllable. Listen and repeat. Then listen and compare.

pep, pebble, bell, better, mellow, melon, well, welfare, fell, fellow, velvet, veteran, then, them, thence, ten, intelligent, terror, tepid, dense, indelicate, seldom, zealous, procession, shed, shell, shelf, shelter, gentle, Jello, jeopardy, treasure, measure, pleasure, check, inject, Chester, let, prelate, president, remedy, rent, prevent, chemical, get, Hester, Hecuba

DRILL III: Twenty words will be read to you. If the word contains the sound of /e/ check it on the list provided; if not, leave it blank. Each word will be spoken twice.

1. bench _____	11. Evelyn _____
2. episode _____	12. escarole _____
3. err _____	13. Edith _____
4. etiquette _____	14. editor _____
5. evening _____	15. been _____
6. appeal _____	16. bare _____
7. pillow _____	17. pearl _____
8. pen _____	18. impeccable _____
9. pencil _____	19. Pentagon _____
10. peace _____	20. Beatles _____

DRILL IV: Listen to the word pairs. Listen and repeat. Then listen and compare.

pit – pet; bit – bet; mitt – met; wit – wet; fill – fell; vintage – vent; thin – then; tin – ten; dip – depth; list – lest; rill – realm; knit – net; sit – set; zip – zeppelin; shin – Shenandoah; chill – cello; ginger – gentleman; kindred – Kenneth; Kim – chem; hiss – Hess; trick – trek

⌐eɪ⌐ As the first part of the rising diphthong /eɪ/ the sound of

/e/ must be accurately pronounced to make a clear diphthong. Students should note the physical movement of the tongue and jaw from the first element to the second. The first sound is held, while the unstressed vowel is closed with a short sharp snap. The cheerleaders "Yea, team" will be more effectively projected if pronounced in this way, thus:

je e e eɪ / tim

DRILL I: Listen for the sound of /eɪ/ at the beginning of the word. Listen and repeat. Then listen and compare.

ape, able, aim, Ava, atheist, ate, aid, ace, Asa, Asia, "h," age, Ajax, ale, ache, ague

DRILL II: Listen for the sound of /eɪ/ in the accented syllable. Listen and repeat. Then listen and compare.

repay, bathe, maiden, wake, fake, invade, they, tailor, trailer, daze, drape, say, slay, insatiable, zany, Shea stadium, chain, jade, name, lame, rain, parade, yea, cake, gate, hate

DRILL III: Twenty words will be read to you. If the word contains the sound of /eɪ/ check it on the list provided; if not, leave it blank. Each word will be spoken twice.

1. appetite _____	11. April _____
2. therefore _____	12. May _____
3. Harvard _____	13. January _____
4. Yale _____	14. favorite _____
5. separation _____	15. Adam _____
6. Jane _____	16. bacon 'n' eggs _____
7. Ada _____	17. playmates _____
8. Jack _____	18. change of pace _____
9. Ann _____	19. daybreak _____
10. manage _____	20. Great Lakes _____

☐ æ ☐ The sound of /æ/ is unique to English, which means that many students of foreign extraction will have difficulty in pronouncing it. It is, moreover, a sound that is peculiarly sensitive to tension, which can cause either an initial glottal stop [ʔæm] "am" or a stiff-throated nasal pronunciation and distortion [ɛ̃əm]. Both pronunciations are poor, but the latter is especially in disfavor and considered an indication of substandard speech. For persons learning to form the sound, two things should be stressed — after, of course, much auditory training. First, the fact that the mouth is more than half open, and second, that the corners of the lips pull back and flatten the aperture.

By any standard, however, the sound is not a mellifluous one. Another type of difficulty it presents is that it has acceptable dialectal variations. It is [æ ʝ ə] in parts of New England and an even broader sound in nonurban Southern speech. It alternates with /a/ in some words, particularly for stage usage. For most students, however, a well-controlled GA /æ/ is essential, and the clinician is well advised to work for it.

DRILL I: Listen for the sound of /æ/ at the beginning of the word. Listen and repeat. Then listen and compare.

apt, apple, abdicate, absence, am, amnesty, affable, after, avenue, attic, attitude, add, addict, answer, ant, aster, asthma, ask, azure, Atcheson, agile, adjunct, Alfred, alimony, arrogant, action, actor, aggravate, Agatha

DRILL II: Listen for the sound of /æ/ in the accented syllable. Listen and repeat. Then listen and compare.

pad, Pakistan, plaque, back, basket, black, man, master, wacky, wax, fantasy, fraction, vacuum, vacillate, evacuate, thank, thatch, than, that, tap, tapestry, trap, intangible, dank, dacron, damask, sand, sachem, sacrifice, slander, Zanzibar, chaperone, sham, shack, chap, challenge, Jack, janitor, knack, navigate, lamb, latter, rattle, rapture, Yankee, captain, candy, clap, classic, gabardine, gastric, glad, happen, hassle

DRILL III: Twenty words will be read to you. If the word contains the sound of /æ/ check it on the list provided; if not, leave it blank. Each word will be spoken twice.

1. chaplain _____	11. artist _____
2. causeway _____	12. Arkansas _____
3. plaid _____	13. Kansas _____
4. Hawaii _____	14. William _____
5. Alaska _____	15. ancestor _____
6. cabbage _____	16. Rebecca _____
7. attend _____	17. manage _____
8. crabapple _____	18. January _____
9. army _____	19. cinnamon _____
10. casualty _____	20. hairy _____

DRILL IV: Listen to the word pairs. Listen and repeat. Then listen and compare.

airy – abbey; pair – patty; prayer – Pratt; bear – bat; Braille – brag; blare – black; Mary * – manly; wary – wacky; fare – fat; vary – vast; there – that; tear (v) – tack; dare – Dan; lair – lack; rare – rack; nary – Nan; Sarah – sand; chair – chat; care – cat; hairy – Hattie; parent – panther; a pair – apparent

(See similar drill in Chapter III, *Techniques of the Drill.*)

| a/aɪ | The sixth and last phoneme of the front vowel scale is not generally taught in public schools *per se,* but only as the first part of the diphthong /aɪ/. In that diphthong it is the crucial sound. The substantial allophones [ɑ‹ɪ] and [ɒɪ], all too com-

* Variants; SA meɪrɪ. Also mærɪ in "spot" dialects.

monly heard, downgrade diction considerably. Suppose you wish to imitate the speech of an uncultured person. You can demonstrate how easy it is to do this by changing the /aɪ/ to [ɑʊɪ] in this phrase: aɪ geɪv ɪm ə pɪs əv maɪ maɪ nd → ɑʊɪ geɪv ɪm ə pɪs əv mɑʊɪ mɑʊɪnd. We see that to have a correct diphthong the student must hear and make a good /a/. Ear training is a first step, followed by the drill below, which will help the student to learn the intermediate sound /a/. It consists of practicing the two tracks without deviating in the pronunciation of the initial sound:

Varying the track of sound as shown below, he will perceive the difference when he makes a substitution:

Another approach to the /aɪ/ is through the sound of /æ/, the phoneme closest to it on the front vowel scale. Instruct the student to pronounce a nonexistent diphthong /æɪ/, then, without changing the shape of the tongue, but opening the mouth a little wider, modify it to /aɪ/. Once sure of the sound, he is ready for the drills.

DRILL I: Listen for the sound of /aɪ/ at the beginning of the word. Listen and repeat. Then listen and compare.

IBM, I'm, Ipana, Eiffel Tower, ivory, item, idea, idle, isotope, ice cream, Inez, iron, aisle, Iris, Irene, irony, iodine, icon, iced, iconoclast

DRILL II: Listen for the sound of /aɪ/ in the accented syllable. Listen and repeat. Then listen and compare.

pilot, pine, bite, bicycle, my, mine, mighty, why, wise, fire, fight, visor, revitalize, thigh, thrice, thine, tiger, retire, dike, Diana, knight, nice, incite, sigh, resign, Zion, shy, Cheyenne, child, chime, gibe, giant, rye, rice, enlighten, liar, kite, kaiser, guide, guise, pliant, client, trial, slice, price, heigh-ho, hire

DRILL III: Twenty words will be read to you. If the word contains the sound of /aɪ/ check it on the list provided; if not, leave it blank. Each word will be spoken twice.

1. pint _____	11. nine _____
2. lint _____	12. poison _____
3. slice _____	13. buy _____
4. seat _____	14. waist _____
5. sit _____	15. kissed _____
6. Ironsides _____	16. hygiene _____
7. tired _____	17. history _____
8. tranquilizer _____	18. dime _____
9. five _____	19. tin _____
10. six _____	20. Ohio _____

THE BACK VOWELS

The back vowels are so named because the back of the tongue is the tensed part, forming a hump toward the velum. To be considered in this section are:

$$u \ ʊ \ o \ (oʊ) \qquad ɔ \ (ɔɪ) \ ɒ \ ɑ \ (ɑʊ)$$

Of these, the first five, that is, all except the /ɑ/ are further characterized by a rounding of the lips which are thrust forward.

u/ʊ The first two phonemes are difficult mainly for students to whom English is a second language. The first vowel is longer, higher, tenser and rounder than the second. It is often combined with /j/ as in /ju/. Both forms will be considered in the drills.

DRILL I: Listen for the sound of /u/ or /ju/ at the beginning of the word. Listen and repeat. Then listen and compare.

oops! Oona, ooze, oodles, Utah, yule, eucharist, uniform, uses, uvula, unit, universe, useful

DRILL II: Listen for the sound of /u/ or /ju/ in the accented syllable. Listen and repeat. Then listen and compare.

pool, repudiate, boost, bugle, woo, whew, moo, remove, remunerate, food, few, voodoo, view, two, true, intuitive, do, drew, bluing, noose, new, Louis, in lieu of, Lusitania, lute, rue, root,* rude, sue, ensue, school, truism, zoo, Zeus, presume, shoot, reshoe, chew, Jewish, rejuvenate, you'll, cool, cruel, ghoul, who, hooligan

DRILL III: Twenty words will be read to you. If the word contains the sounds of /u/ or /ju/ check it on the list provided; if not, leave it blank. Each word will be spoken twice.

1. juicy _____	8. wood _____	15. beauty _____
2. goose _____	9. wouldn't _____	16. imbue _____
3. under _____	10. Ural _____	17. boots _____
4. over _____	11. ouster _____	18. shoes _____
5. June _____	12. cloister _____	19. rubbers _____
6. whose _____	13. through _____	20. July _____
7. Hugh _____	14. thorough _____	

DRILL IV: Listen to the word pairs. Listen and repeat. Then listen and compare.

Pulitzer – pull; boot – bull; woo – wool; flute – foot; two –

* Variant: rʊt.

110

took; new – nook; loose – look; ruse – rook; soon – forsook; shoe –shook; coo – cook; who – hook

☐ ʊ ☐ The second back vowel as described is less rounded, less tense, and lower than the first back vowel. Because it occurs less frequently than either /u/ or /ʌ/, students sometimes find it difficult to recognize.

DRILL I: Listen for the sound of /ʊ/ in the accented syllable. Listen and repeat. Then listen and compare.

push, pullet, book, bullet, wool, worsted, full, fuller, took, nook, forsook, sugar, should, look, rook, cook, cookie, crook, good, should

DRILL II: Twenty words will be read to you If the word contains the sound of /ʊ/ check it on the list provided; if not, leave it blank. Each word will be spoken twice.

1. bookish _____	11. foot _____
2. bulletin _____	12. boot _____
3. business _____	13. bustle _____
4. bully _____	14. woman _____
5. beauty _____	15. women _____
6. wolf _____	16. pussy _____
7. would _____	17. pony _____
8. won't _____	18. cushion _____
9. wonder _____	19. cool _____
10. woe _____	20. Worcester _____

DRILL III: Listen to the word pairs. Listen and repeat. Then listen and compare.

book – buck; pool – pulverize; put – puddle; full – fun; wool – won; took – ton; hook – hung; soot – sunk; shook – shuck; nook – none; look – luck; rook – run; cook – cunning; good – gun

111

o/ou The third phoneme /o/ exists both as a single sound and more commonly as part of the diphthong /ou/. As a single sound it is found in unaccented syllables, *e.g., hotel* /hotel'/ and as a variant before voiceless consonants, *e.g., No Strings* /no strɪŋz/. More precisely, it is the allophone [oᴛ], a weakened vowel. It is substandard to weaken it further when it is unstressed and the last sound of a word: (Do not substitute /ə/.)

Pogo, piano, bellow, borrow, callow, Eldorado, follow, hello, Jello, mellow, pillow, sorrow, Shiloh, jabot, Petro, yarrow, tallow, Tasso, window

Careful usage prefers /o/ in the first syllable of the following words, although the sound of the schwa is also heard throughout the land:

obese, obey, opaque, opinion, Olympic, omit, omega, overt

It is interesting to note in relation to the fluxion of sounds that the full value of the diphthong tends to remain in proper names such as Orion, Osage, Osiris, Ozymandias; it has taken on a common variant pronunciation /ɔ/ in *oral, oration,* and *oriental.*

The mispronunciation of the diphthong, however, is our concern. The sound /ou/ is especially difficult for students of ESL (English as a Second Language) who fail to give it both proper length and proper rounding. Improperly pronounced, it will impart a flavor of foreignism to anybody's speech. Try, for instance, the sentence "No, I can't go to Coney Island" with the sound of /ʌ/ substituted for the /ou/: nʌ / aɪ kænt gʌ tə kʌnɪ aɪlənd. Students should be directed to watch the lip formation for /ou/ in a mirror, to see the lips form a definite oval and then close more tightly in a pursed position for the second, unstressed vowel. Eye training for this sound is a useful variant of ear training. The students "keep score" of the number of /ou/ sounds

112

they see made in a sequence of twenty assorted vowels by watching the mouth. (Listening is not prohibited.)

i ou ɑu ɔi ɒ o u

ou u ou ei ai o̞ ou

ou ɑ ɑu ɔ ou ɔ

DRILL I: Listen for the sound of /ou/ at the beginning of the word. Listen and repeat. Then listen and compare.

oak, open, oboe, oval, over, oath, odor, only, ode, ocean, ogle, ogre, old, omen, onus, ozone, otophone

DRILL II: Listen for the sound of /ou/ in the accented syllable. Listen and repeat. Then listen and compare.

prone, poem, bone, blow, moat, remote, work, whoa, telephone, vote, though, those, thorough, token, doze, nose, loaded, erosion, soldier, zone, zodiac, shone, chose, joke, Joe, yolk, coke, croak, ghost, hose, host, home

DRILL III: Twenty words will be read to you. If the word contains the sound of /ou/ check it on the list provided; if not, leave it blank. Each word will be spoken twice.

1. colony _____	11. Top Job _____
2. pony _____	12. Tony _____
3. Rose _____	13. Anthony _____
4. oppose _____	14. sew _____
5. today _____	15. Sophie _____
6. moose _____	16. Johnson _____
7. Oakhurst _____	17. Monroe _____
8. Ohio _____	18. Tom _____
9. Tokyo _____	19. Joan _____
10. Joseph _____	20. Mr. Jones _____

DRILL IV: Listen to the word pairs. Listen and repeat. Then listen and compare.

pall – pole; ball – bowl; maul – mole; wall – woe; fall – foal; vault – vote; thrall – throw; tall – toll; daw – dole; gnaw – knoll; law – loll; raw – roll; saw – sole; shawl – shoal; chore – choke; jaw – joke; cord – coke; gore – goad

 ɔ/ɔɪ The phonetic symbol of the fourth back phoneme /ɔ/ is representational art. It mirrors the shape the lips take in forming an open, tense, forward thrust. Even a slight relaxation of the lips in making the sound imparts a slovenly aspect to diction, that is, the use of [ɔ͜] in "all" or "always" is substandard. The sound is subject to another common mispronunciation when it appears at the end of a syllable, as in *drawing*, or at the end of a word, as in *law* or *Arkansas*. We willingly concede to our students the probable reason for the mispronunciation — man's natural dislike of remaining with his mouth open, a position suggesting a dumb, questioning attitude. That is why some people succumb to the temptation to add a natural closing for the position, the inverted (*r* type) pronunciation so that *law* becomes lɔ; *drawing room* drɔ́ɪŋ rum, and *Arkansas* arkɪnsɔ́. The clinician has no choice but to state, categorically, that where there is no *r* in the spelling, these pronunciations are not acceptable.*

DRILL I: Listen for the sounds of /ɔ/ or /ɔɪ/ at the beginning of the word. Listen and repeat. Then listen and compare.

or, orb, orbit, awe, order, orphan, officer, Austria, autopsy, orchid, organize, orthodox, organ, ordinary, alter, always, Australia, Audubon, audible, inaudible

DRILL II: Listen for the sounds of /ɔ/ or /ɔɪ/ in the accented syllable. Listen and repeat. Then listen and compare.

* But characteristic of "spot" dialects. President John Kennedy used the inverted pronunciation.

paw, pawn, applaud, Paul, ball, boss, brought, brown, maudlin, moss, mortar, Walter, false, ford, floored, vaunt, vault, Thor, thoughtful, taunt, toss, talked, daughter, adorable, draw, saw, saucer, resources, naughty, nought, law, laud, applaud, lost, raw, Raleigh, raucous, Shaw, Shawnee, chore, chalk, jaw, jaundice, your, yawn, caught, cost, cord, quarter, gore, Gordon, gaudy, haughty

DRILL III: Twenty words will be read to you. If the word contains the sounds of /ɔ/ or /ɔ˞/ check it on the list provided; if not, leave it blank. Each word will be spoken twice.

1. nautical ____	8. warm ____	15. Joel ____
2. Norman ____	9. often ____ *	16. always ____
3. not ____	10. cough ____	17. almost ____
4. soccer ____	11. author ____	18. after ____
5. bowling ____	12. George ____	19. over ____
6. corn ____	13. Jack ____	20. shawl ____
7. broccoli ____	14. Jock ____	

DRILL IV: Listen to word pairs. Listen and repeat. Then listen and compare.

pall – pole; ball – bowl; maul – mole; wall – woe; fall – foal; vault – vote; thrall – throw; tall – toll; daw – doe; gnaw – know; law – loll; raw – role; saw – soul; shawl – shoal; chore – choke; jaw – joke; cord – code; gore – goad

There is considerable variation in the pronunciation of /ɔ/ shifting between /ou/ and /ɒ/. Words like *oral* and *oration* are pronounced with the sound of /ou/ by some, but with an /ɔ/ by others. *Laurence* is pronounced either with /ɔ/ or with /ɒ/, as are *laurel* and *orange*, nor is the usage determined strictly by localities. Even authorities differ, one stating that the GA pro-

* The clinician must exercise discretion in accepting variants. Before voiceless fricatives, g or ng /ɔ/ or /ɒ/ are acceptable.

nunciation of *forehead* is fɔrɪd, another that it is fɒrɪd. The pronunciation of *water* varies within fifty miles in the same state from wɔtɚ to wɒtɚ. The clinician is well advised to work for good quality in the sound and for the elimination of substandard pronunciations only.

The diphthong composed of the phoneme /ɔ/ and a weak vowel /ɔɪ/ is characteristically mispronounced /ɝ/ and vice versa /ɝ/ is mispronounced /ɔɪ/ and even more commonly /ʌɪ/. If such mispronunciations exist in the group, they must be attacked through auditory discrimination drill, analysis, and practice. Examples of the mispronunciations are: "enjoying oneself in Jersey" as ɪndʒɝ́ɪŋ wʌnself ɪn dʒɔɪzɪ; "oil in the ointment" as ɝ̩l ɪn ðɪ ʌɪntmənt.

DRILL I: Listen for the sound of /ɔɪ/ in the accented syllable. Listen and repeat. Then listen and compare.

oil, oily, oyster, ointment, poison, boisterous, moist, foil, avoid, toil, doily, noise, loiter, royal, royally, soil, soybean, choice, Joyce, rejoice, yoicks, coil, recoil, goiter, hoity-toity

DRILL II: Twenty words will be read to you. If the word contains the sound of /ɔɪ/ check it on the list provided. If not, leave it blank. Each word will be spoken twice.

1. alley _____	11. boysenberry _____
2. ally _____	12. Lloyd _____
3. rejoin _____	13. Flo _____
4. verse _____	14. Floyd _____
5. universe _____	15. Roy _____
6. tinfoil _____	16. first _____
7. soil _____	17. third _____
8. cloister _____	18. Oregon _____
9. odor _____	19. invoice _____
10. order _____	20. embroider _____

DRILL III: Listen to the word pairs. Listen and repeat. Then listen and compare.

oil – earl;   poison – pearl;   boil – burly;   foil – furl;   avoid – averse;   toil – turn;   doit – dirt;   soil – assert;   joy – germ; choice – churn;   coy – incur;   goiter – girder

The fifth phoneme /ɒ/ may be approached either by forming the sound of /ɑ/ with the mouth in the /ɔ/ position, or the sound of /ɔ/ with the mouth in the /ɑ/ position.
Edward Lear has presented the sound humorously:

THE AHKOND OF SWAT *

Is he wise or foolish, young or old?
  Does he drink his soup and his coffee cold,
          . . . . or Hot,
        The Ahkond of Swat?

Does he wear a turban, a fez, or a hat?
  Does he sleep on a mattress, a bed, or a mat,
          . . . . or a Cot.
        The Ahkond of Swat?

When he writes copy in round hand size,
  Does he cross his t's and finish his i's
          . . . . with a Dot,
        The Ahkond of Swat?

Does he study the wants of his own dominion,
  Or doesn't he care for public opinion
          . . . . a Jot,
        The Ahkond of Swat?

Is he quiet, or always making a fuss?
  Is his steward a Swiss or a Swede or a Russ,
          . . . . or a Scot,
        The Ahkond of Swat?

* Reprinted from *The Complete Nonsense Book* by Edward Lear by permission of the Publisher, Dodd, Mead & Company, and by permission of the Administrators of Constance S. Esther Rosa Cipelletti Lady Strachie deceased.

117

Does he wear a white tie when he dines with his friends,
And tie it neat in a bow with ends
. . . . or a Knot?
The Ahkond of Swat?

Does he like new cream and hate mince pies?
When he looks at the sun does he wink his eyes,
. . . . or not
The Ahkond of Swat?

Some one, or nobody knows, I wot
Who, or which, or why or what,
. . . . or WHAT
IS THE AHKOND OF SWAT?

— EDWARD LEAR

DRILL I: Listen for the sound of /ɒ/ at the beginning of the word. Listen and repeat. Then listen and compare.

object (n), obligate, oculist, octane, odd, optimist, oxygen, on, otter, oxen, oncoming, opportunity, olive, osteopath

DRILL II: Listen for the sound of /ɒ/ in the accented syllable. Listen and repeat. Then listen and compare.

possible, ponder, opossum, dock, tot, cop, cod, cottage, lobster, modern, horrible, responsive, shot, throng, volley, intoxicate, fondly, quarrel, trotting, stopping, authority

DRILL III: Twenty words will be read to you. If the word contains the sound of /ɒ/ check it on the list provided; if not, leave it blank. Each word will be spoken twice.

1. borrow _____	6. Iowa _____
2. barrel _____	7. Ontario _____
3. borough _____	8. utopia _____
4. wasp _____	9. Watusi _____
5. papa _____	10. Wyoming _____

11. watch _____	16. squab _____
12. Olga _____	17. fraud _____
13. August _____	18. honor _____
14. shock _____	19. bomb _____
15. outlaws _____	20. orchard _____

The sound is well practiced in comparative lists with /ɑ/, as in the next section on /ɑ/, and with /ɔ/ and /ʌ/ below:

DRILL IV /ɔ/ AND /ɒ/: Listen to the word pairs. Listen and repeat. Then listen and compare.

paw – pocket; balk – bock; walk – what; malt – mock; fault – foster; * vault – volume; talk – tot; daughter – dot; nought – not; law – lot; raw – rot; saw – sot; shore – shot; chalk – chop; jaw – jot; yore – yacht; core – cot; gore – got; hoar – hot

/ɒ/ AND /ʌ/:

pocket – pucker; bock – buck; mock – amuck; what – won; flock – flutter; tot – tuck; dock – duck; sock – suck; shock – shuck; chop – chuck; jot – jut; cock – cuckold; clock – clutter; got – gut

$\boxed{\text{ɑ/ɑʊ}}$ The last of the back phonemes, /ɑ/, the unrounded one, the one that every doctor uses to make the oral cavity visible, is indeed a sigh of relief. It is the most universal sound of the letter *a* and familiar to Spaniards, Italians, Slavs, Germans, and Englishmen alike, and for that reason most often substituted by them for /æ/. It should impart to speech by itself, and as the first part of the diphthong /ɑʊ/, a soft, flowing quality. It can be pronounced correctly only when the mouth is both open and relaxed. It sometimes involves a curious mispronunciation when the fifth phoneme, /ɒ/, is substituted for it. Like the mispro-

* Variant: fɔstɚ.

119

nunciation of the *ng*, this is one of the last frontiers of lingering foreignism. We hear the phrase "part silver, part gold" as if it were "pot silver, pot gold." The clinician will therefore stress careful listening and awareness of the kinesthesia of the sound.

DRILL I: Listen to the sound of /ɑ/ or /ɑʊ/ at the beginning of the word. Listen and repeat. Then listen and compare.

alms, art, ardor, arson, army, Arthur, Arkansas, Armageddon, aunt, archeology, arc, arch, arbor, arbitrate

DRILL II: Listen for the sound of /ɑ/ or /ɑʊ/ in the accented syllable. Listen and repeat. Then listen and compare.

part, impart, bard, barter, mart, remark, martyr, warrant, afar, farthing, farmer, varmint, varnish, Tahoe, dark, darling, lark, rama, dram, sari, Zsa-Zsa, charm, Charlie, jargon, Charlotte, yard, yardage, car, calm, garden, guardian, harken, psalm

DRILL III: Twenty words will be read to you. If the word contains the sounds of /ɑ/ or /ɑʊ/ check it on the list provided; if not, leave it blank. Each word will be spoken twice.

1. Alma _____	11. bottom _____
2. Amy _____	12. pocket _____
3. Arthur _____	13. jacket _____
4. Andrew _____	14. Palmolive _____
5. Aruba _____	15. ramparts _____
6. Prague _____	16. Abilene _____
7. Dakota _____	17. Florida _____
8. San Francisco _____	18. parkway _____
9. Mah Jongg _____	19. guard _____
10. parlor _____	20. Washington _____

DRILL IV: Listen to the word pairs. Listen and repeat. Then listen and compare.

pot – part; odd – art; block – blarney; mock – mark; what – wampum; fond – farm; tot – tart; dot – dart; lock – lark; sock – psalm; chop – charm; Jock – jargon; yacht – yard; cop – carp; got – garter; hock – hark

The diphthong /ɑʊ/, Hollywood's darling,* is considerably mutilated when it becomes /æʊ/. Much is also lost from the quality of speech. An animated cartoon once capitalized on this mispronunciation by exaggerating the words "Not now" and using /æʊ/ in imitation of a night-prowling cat. James Joyce recognized its affiliation with the feline when he spelled his cat's mew mgniau. In practicing the diphthong, the crucial sound is the first. A full, open, relaxed /ɑ/ is the determinant of a good /ɑʊ/.

DRILL I: Listen for the sound of /ɑʊ/ at the beginning of the word. Listen and repeat. Then listen and compare.

owl, ouster, out, outer, outermost, our, ounce, outbreak, ouch, outcry, outside

DRILL II: Listen for the sound of /ɑʊ/ in the accented syllable. Listen and repeat. Then listen and compare.

pounce, prowl, bounce, brown, mound, wow, flounce, avow, town, trowel, down, drown, dowdy, sound, Strauss, resound, shout, chowder, jowl, noun, renown, loud, louder, lounge, rouse, cowl, growl

DRILL III: Twenty words will be read to you. If the word contains the sound of /ɑʊ/ check it on the list provided; if not, leave it blank. Each word will be spoken twice.

* "How now, brown cow" is reputed to be daily voice practice for starlets.

121

1. Ireland ____	11. up ____
2. Austria ____	12. down ____
3. boundary ____	13. loud ____
4. crowded ____	14. bough ____
5. doubt ____	15. bought ____
6. purrs ____	16. ground ____
7. butt ____	17. powder ____
8. about ____	18. meow ____
9. Howard ____	19. bow-wow ____
10. coward ____	20. mouse ____

DRILL IV: Listen to the word pairs. Listen and repeat. Then listen and compare.

pock – pound; bock – bound; mock – mouse; what – wound; flock – flounder; Tom – town; Don – down; sock – sound; stock – astound; chop – chow; job – jowl; cop – cowl; grotto – growl; hot – howl

⬚ 3/ɝ ⬚ The mid-vowel /ɝ/, as pointed out in Chapter II, is the end product of an evolutionary process. It may be correctly pronounced with or without inversion, although we recommend the inverted form (GA) for students who find it difficult to control the sound. Holding the normal bite position lightly will often help produce a correct sound.

DRILL I: Listen to the sound of /ɝ/ at the beginning of the word. Listen and repeat. Then listen and compare.

err, irk, urn, earth, early, earthen, urchin, Ursula, erg, ergot, Ernest, herb, urban, ermine, Irwin

DRILL II: Listen to the sound of /ɝ/ in the accented syllable. Listen and repeat. Then listen and compare.

purr, purpose, burr, burden, mercy, murder, whirr, worse, fur, fertile, flirt, verse, verdant, third, thirsty, worthy, turn, turtle, dirt, derma, certain, assert, stir, slur, shirt, Shirley, churn, church, journey, Jurgen, nurture, lurch, curl, curfew, girl, Gertrude, return, impersonal

DRILL III: Twenty words will be read to you. If the word contains the sound of /ɝ/ check it on the list provided; if not, leave it blank. Each word will be spoken twice.

1. learn _____
2. French _____
3. Russian _____
4. prefer _____
5. preference _____
6. lurk _____
7. lunch _____
8. never _____
9. under _____
10. were _____

11. Irma _____
12. cousin _____
13. circus _____
14. theater _____
15. nurture _____
16. nurse _____
17. worse _____
18. hearse _____
19. cemetery _____
20. Wyatt Earp _____

DRILL IV: Listen to the word pairs. Listen and repeat. Then listen and compare.

perk – putt; burden – butter; murky – mutt; ferny – funny; third – thud; turkey – touchy; dirt – duck; serf – sup; shirt – shut; churn – chug; jersey – juts; nerve – nut; lurk – luck; curl – cut; girl – gut; hurl – hut

☐ ə ☐ The reader is referred to Chapter II for a discussion of the sound of /ə/, the schwa. It may be brought to the students' attention that the schwa can barely be heard — that, in fact, its use in a word serves the purpose of shortening the word. Additional drills are provided here:

DRILL I: Listen for the sound of /ə/ at the beginning of the word. Listen and repeat. Then listen and compare.

upon, about, among, aware, awhile, afloat, avoid, athwart, attack, ado, asleep, ashore, achieve, adjust, anew, alas, alack, around, arouse, accord, aglow, agree

DRILL II: Listen for the sound of /ə/ in the final syllable. Listen and repeat. Then listen and compare.

mamma, papa, vanilla, soda, Alabama, Florida, Dakota, drama, cinema, orchestra, tuba, gorilla, zebra

Listen for the sound of /ə/ medially. Listen and repeat. Then listen and compare.

secretary, library, February, necessary, emphasis, syllable, vegetable, tentative, history, geography, buffalo, giraffe, international, intervene

DRILL III: Twenty words will be read to you. If the word contains a schwa /ə/ or /ɚ/ check it on the list provided; if not, leave it blank. Each word will be spoken twice.

1. apple _____	11. circus _____
2. appeal _____	12. famous _____
3. abdicate _____	13. Robert _____
4. abide _____	14. Anna _____
5. amity _____	15. Ann _____
6. among _____	16. Kalamazoo _____
7. art _____	17. Rhode Island _____
8. artfully _____	18. Paris _____
9. chocolate _____	19. mathematics _____
10. flavor _____	20. arithmetic _____

124

⌐ ʌ ⌐ The last of the mid-vowel phonemes /ʌ/ is frequently confused with /ɒ/ or with /o/ by Spanish speakers, a mispronunciation that constitutes a foreignism. It is a colorless, flat, open sound, the tongue low as for /ɑ/ and the muscular impulse and tension placed farther forward. Ear training and comparative drills are essential in learning to differentiate the sound. Students may note that it is only slightly weakened when unstressed at the beginning of a word.

DRILL I: Listen for the sound of /ʌ/ at the beginning of the word. Listen and repeat. Then listen and compare.

up, upset, upkeep, under, ugly, us, ultimate, other, udder, ulcer, ultra, ultramodern, umbrella, umpire, unashamed, unacceptable, unadvisable, unapplicable, unwilling, untruth

DRILL II: Listen for the sound of /ʌ/ in the accented syllable. Listen and repeat. Then listen and compare.

pump, plump, bump, brunt, mumps, won, wonder, fun, front, ton, tunnel, done, dump, dunce, sum, sumptuous, resumption, shun, chuck, chuckle, jug, jugular, junction, justice, none, renunciation, lung, lunge, rug, rump, young, youngster, cut, custard, Andy Gump, gutter, guttural

DRILL III: Twenty words will be read to you. If the word contains the sound of /ʌ/ check it on the list provided; if not, leave it blank. Each word will be spoken twice.

1. tongue _____	7. puncture _____
2. song _____	8. prune _____
3. sung _____	9. pocket _____
4. sunny _____	10. pooch
5. graduation _____	11. uncle _____
6. monkey _____	12. cousin _____

13. aunt _____	17. mother _____
14. brother _____	18. putt _____
15. mommy _____	19. put _____
16. mummy _____	20. dedication _____

DRILL IV: Listen to the word groups. Listen and repeat. Then listen and compare.

pot – put – putt; bock – book – buck; shock – shook – shuck; shot – should – shut; lock – look – luck; cod – could – cud; mock – moot – mutt; bomb – boom – bum; pop – poop – pub; roster – rooster – rusty

An interesting variant of Drill III is to give each student two copies of the drill. Ask him to answer one silently and by himself. The second one will then be read. The comparison of results should prove fruitful.

THE FALLING DIPHTHONG

The falling diphthongs ɪə ɛə ɔə ʊə are so called because the second, unstressed, sound – the schwa, or schwa inverted – is lower than the first. These pronunciations, like the /ɝ/ sound, are an end product in the evolution of the r and streamline pronunciation. They have made one syllable from two and substituted a less tense for a more tense vowel. As near to us historically as the fifteenth century, words like *peer, pair, pour,* and *poor* were pronounced: piɚ peɪɚ poɚ puɚ. They are now: pɪɚ pɛɚ pɔɚ puɚ. Correctly made, they impart a lightness to speech. Clinicians should work for this quality. Confusions between /ɪɚ/ and /ɛɚ/, as between /ɔɚ/ and /ʊɚ/, are not uncommon. Eartraining drills should precede practice on the comparative list below. (Homonyms have been included. Students of ESL enjoy pointing them out.)

126

Iɚ	ɛɚ	ɔɚ	ʊɚ
peer	pair	pour	poor
beer (bier)	bear (bare)	bore (boar)	boor (Boer)
weir (we're)	wear	wore	wooer *
mere	mare	more	moor
fear	fare (fair)	fore (four)	fewer * /fjʊə/
tear (n)	tear (v)	tore	tour
dear (deer)	dare	door	dour (doer)
sere (seer)	Sarah	sore	sewer *
shear (sheer)	share	shore	sure
cheer	chair	chore	chewer *
near	ne'er	nor	newer *
leer (Lear)	lair	lore	lure
rear	rare	roar	Ruhr
year	yare	yore	you're
gear	guerre (Fr.)	gore	gluer *
hear	hair	hoar	who're

A useful "game" is for the clinician to use only three or four lines of the drill and to challenge the students to compose the others.

* In words adding the suffix er, the first vowel retains a longer pronunciation.

VIII

Articulation Difficulties: Consonants

————◆————

There is a pedagogic as well as a logical advantage in limiting the term "articulation" to consonants, particularly at the time when students are being introduced to the science and dynamics of the production of sounds. It permits a distinction between the specific loci of consonant production and the relative shapings of the vowels in the mouth. We will use the term in that sense. In most clinics for substandard speech, the pressure of time is such that the clinician bypasses teaching the formation of all consonants and their points of articulation in favor of concentrating on the common errors the group is making. A compromise system that has been found effective is to teach the concepts of articulation, present the framework of the consonant chart, and locate the sounds actually studied on it. Then, if time allows, the sounds not specifically studied can be added. This procedure gives considerably more meaning to the chart.

MANNER OF EMISSION	PLACE OF ARTICULATION						
NASAL	m			n		ŋ	
PLOSIVE	p b			t d		k g	
FRICATIVE	ʍ w	f	ʋ θ ð	r j ʌ z	ʃ ʒ		h
FRICATIVE BLENDS				tʃ dʒ			
LATERAL				l			
	LABIAL	LABIODENTAL	DENTAL	ALVEOLAR	PALATAL	VELAR	GLOTTAL

THE CONSONANT CHART

As the chart indicates, consonants have three descriptive characteristics: *voicing, enunciation,* and *place* of articulation. As to the first, they are either voiceless or voiced, depending on whether the vocal cords are in vibration. An amusing story is told of a proctor at an examination in speech who suddenly sees student after student clutch at his throat. They were testing, in the time-honored way, for voiced or voiceless sounds. There are four general ways in which the stream of air is expelled during the formation of consonants: *nasally,* where the air is stopped in the mouth but emitted through the nasal passage and nose; *plosively,* where the air is cut off from the nasal passage by the lifting of the velum, stopped entirely at the point of articulation, and then forced out in a small pressure pellet; *fricatively,* where the organs of articulation make a narrow funnel through which the air filters in a narrow stream. The resultant friction has an element of noise which distinguishes these consonants. There is a single *lateral* phoneme in English — the /l/ — in which the air flows over the sides of the tongue. The /w/ and /r/ are often

129

called "glides," but making that distinction is not productive with students in school, so that we include them with the fricatives. The third characteristic, place of articulation, of which there are seven, consists of the two articulating organs or articulatory parts that control the flow of air. They are listed below, beginning with the most outward and visible point and moving inward.

1. Lip to lip (bilabials)
2. Lower lip to upper teeth (labiodental)
3. Tongue-tip to teeth (dental)
4. Tongue-tip to gum ridge (alveolar)
5. Mid-tongue to palate (palatal)
6. Back of tongue to velum (velar)
7. Glottis (glottal)

COMMON MISPRONUNCIATIONS

$\boxed{\text{w/м}}$ [1] The distinction between these sounds, although useful and agreeable, is generally taught only in special schools such as performing arts, and in some classes. A teaching device producing instant recognition of the contrast between the sounds is to let the student feel the difference in the emission of the air on the back of his hand. Since this method may have a practical drawback, the clinician can also demonstrate the difference in the strength of the air pressure of the /м/ by holding a small slip of paper before his lips as he speaks the sounds. The paper will flutter for the /м/. The difference between the words on the comparative list is not only a phonemic but often an onomatopoetic one.

COMPARATIVE DRILL: /w/ AND /м/

wine – whine;   wear – where;   wile – while;   wail – whale;
weal – wheel;   wight – white;   wacky – whack;   wizard – whiz;

[1] A distinction is often made between /hw/, partly voiceless, and /м/, entirely voiceless.

"y" – why; wet – whet; went – when; watt – what; witch – which; weather – whether; win – whinny; wither – whither; wig – Whig; woo – whew; women – whim; were – whir; wisp – whisper

| f/v | The use of the lower lip only in /f/ and /v/ poses a particular hardship for Spanish-speaking people, who confuse it with a parallel two-lip sound in Spanish. Here eye training and kinesthesia are the clinician's allies. See the comparative drill /f, v-p, b/ in Chapter III.

DRILL I: Listen for the sound of /f/ and /v/ at the beginning of the word. Listen and repeat. Then listen and compare.

fee, fit, fend, fare, fat, fine, food, foot, foe, fall, fob, far, fun, fern, flee, flit, phlegm, flare, flat, flight, flow, flaw, flock, flower, flood, flirt, free, fritter, fret, fright, fruit, froze, fraught, frock, front, furs; veal, vintage, vent, vat, vile, view, vote, vaunt, vocative, varnish, verse, venal, vision, verify, vanquish, vibrate, viewer, volt, vault, vomit, vase, Vernon

DRILL II: Listen for the sound of /f/ or /v/ in the accented syllable. Listen and repeat. Then listen and compare.

offer, refer, prefer, suffer, toughness, inform, conform, reform, belief, skiff, effect, after, perfume, leaf, inverse, reverse, perverse, invalid, reveal, pervade, reveal, revision, revert, reverse, revenge, revive, revamp, review, revoke, revolt

| θ/ð | The only consonants made on the front teeth in English are the /θ/ and /ð/. Very few students know this fact. In substandard speech a dentalized [t̪] and [d̪] respectively are substituted for them in what has come to be known as "New Yorkese." To make the sounds of /θ/ and /ð/ correctly, the tip of the tongue delicately intercedes in the flow of air behind the

131

upper teeth. The teeth are parted slightly. This is a better kinesthetic concept than the clumsy one often given young children
that the sounds are made "between the teeth." Students in elementary or high schools who have trouble in forming these
sounds should be cautioned not to try to push the air out, but
to hold back and let it flow in a thin stream over the tongue-tip
and out between the teeth. There may be organic reasons for the
mispronunciation such as macroglossia, tongue thrust, dental or
acoustic abnormalities which must be considered first, but many
of the mispronunciations heard originate from poor speech habits
or from imitation. Properly motivated, students can learn to use
the correct sound. It is recommended that a mobility exercise
(see Chapter III) be used first, followed by comparative drills
and readings.

DRILL:

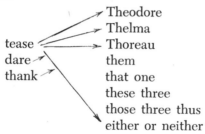

tease
dare
thank

Theodore
Thelma
Thoreau
them
that one
these three
those three thus
either or neither

COMPARATIVE DRILL: /t-d/ AND /θ-ð/

disease – these; tick – thick; till – thrill; den – then; dare –
there; Dan – than; attach – thatch; die – thy; drew – through;
doe – though; taught – thought; tundra – thunder; tread –
thread; tank – thank; talis – thallus; tame – thane; tanker –
thanker; tank full – thankful; tort – athwart; team – theme;
deed – thee; dense – thence; term – thermos; dare – there;
too – thew; day – they; tie – thigh; Tim will – thimble; tin –
thin; dine – thine; ting – thing; tinker – thinker; turtle –

132

third; turf – thirst; distrophy – this trophy; tore – Thor; torn – thorn; endow – thou; trace – Thrace; Townsend – thousand; trash – thrash; trawler – thrall; tread – thread; tree – three; trust – thrust; tummy – thumb; dust – thus

| t/d | To speak English with distinction one must be able to form an aspirated or clear /t/. This in turn depends on precise control of the tip of the tongue. If students do not possess the ability to do this, it is very likely that their speech will show evidences of other substandard pronunciations, omissions, or inadequacies. The sound of /tʰ/ is not a sound that can be learned at first try. Three conditions must precede its acquisition:

1. Acoustic perception and kinesthetic understanding of the sound.
2. An impelling motivation to improve one's speech.
3. Self-discipline to submit to rigorous practice.

Clinicians are aware of this and take particular care to motivate the study of these sounds, using time-honored ideas or whatever their ingenuity can adduce:

- that clearness of diction is required in many average occupations such as sales person, telephone operator, office worker, astronaut, as well as in the growing communications industry.
- that there are unwritten social distinctions based upon diction.
- that a person's speech should reflect the best of the community whether one plans to attend college or not.

We should like to add a favorite reason of ours. Democracy means, among other things, that people have a choice. This is certainly true for young people in school, when their minds are open to receive and their muscles able to adapt. If they acquire

133

the ability to speak better now, and later find it of little practical use — no great loss. How tragic, on the contrary, when a person has unnecessarily limited himself to local, dialectal, or peer-group speech and then finds he needs a more universal speech when he is no longer as adaptable to learning!

The sounds of /t/ and /d/, voiceless and voiced, respectively, are articulated by the tongue-tip touching the upper gum ridge preparatory to plosive emission. Place them on the consonant chart in the appropriate box (see chart at end of this chapter). The voiceless plosives are always more forceful than the voiced. They are not, however, aspirated in all positions. Here is a first ear-training drill.

DRILL I: Ask your students, by listening carefully, to try to recognize the words pronounced with the aspirated /t/. As you read them, have students check such words on the list provided and leave the others blank. Correct the lists. Can they determine in what positions the /t/ is aspirated?

1. ten _____	11. Tim _____
2. twelve _____	12. trim _____
3. dent _____	13. the cot is here _____
4. dentist _____	14. cotton _____
5. tress _____	15. cat _____
6. little _____	16. cattle _____
7. letter _____	17. pontoon _____
8. Lent _____	18. asked _____
9. tip _____	19. tackle _____
10. tee _____	20. August _____

If you have followed through carefully, the students should have discovered that:

1. /t/ is aspirated when it is a final sound, or when it is followed by a vowel sound — *ten, Lent,* etc.

2. It is not aspirated when followed by a consonant — *twelve, trick,* etc.

3. It seems to blur in words like *little* and *cotton.*

If the students are able to hear these things, they are well on their way and ready for a mobility drill; namely, the basic drills on /t/ and /d/. Not only will the clinician introduce this drill frequently, but the students should work on it by themselves at least fifteen minutes a week. Further drill can be provided by a circular, or chain, procedure which is coupled with everyday information. For example: Where did you eat today? (the lead question). Answers include any place name containing an aspirate /t/: Timbuktu, Dakota, Matteawan, Turkey, Schenectady, and so on.

Students may like to compose for themselves lists in which the /t^h/ is initial, medial, and final. Sometimes they prefer limiting the area to which the words apply:

Area	Initial	Medial	Final
love	tender	hotter	heart (carat?)
school	teacher	intelligence	passed (flunked?)
hunting	tension	artillery	shot
camp	tent	beating	overnight
cooking	teaspoon	platter	burnt
home	tired	painting	slept
garden	tied the roses	watered	peat
baseball	time	batter	out
English	topic	grammatical	wrote
geography	topography	plateau	east and west
fishing	towline	netted	caught

In practice, the initial position should be drilled first, then the final one. The medial is the most difficult, particularly where the accent does not fall on the syllable containing the /t^h/. A firm but very light aspirate must be mastered. Lists can be expanded by adding phrases such as "tell me . . ." or ". . . is too bad" initially and finally. Numbers ending in -ty and the multiplication tables are also grist for this mill. Constructing phrases with several aspirates can evoke imaginative responses. Here are some:

- tell a tale or two
- temptation is as temptation does
- today, tomorrow and always
- white, tan and terra cotta
- retarded the gas and braked
- Timothy Tall and Mathilda Short
- Tappan Zee and Washington bridges
- autumn and winter

The sound of /t/ is also unaspirated when it is followed by a consonant in the next word in the same breath group. Narrow transcription would indicate this /t,/, but broad transcription, which we use, indicates neither aspirated nor unaspirated modifications.

DRILL II: Ask students to listen for and then try to make these distinctions.

tea – tree; tip – trip; tap – trap; hot evening – hot summer; went out – went looking; quite orderly – quiet Don

We have started this section with positive thinking but we must now give a name to the most common mispronunciation of the /t/ and /d/: *dentalization*. As the word suggests, the sounds are made with the tongue pressing against the teeth rather than on the gum ridge. What is also true is that the blade of the tongue is used instead of the tip and that the pressure is firm instead of light. The students may have heard people of Slavic background make such *t*'s and *d*'s. Were they to learn Russian,

136

they would have to practice dentalized _t_'s and _d_'s, just as they now work for alveolar placement. The only exception in English to a high-placed /t/ and /d/ occurs in movement, when they are followed by /θ/ or /ð/, in which case, in anticipation of the forward sound, they are pronounced on the teeth. This is a language phenomenon called _assimilation_. Examples: cut_ them close, wide _thongs, wind threatens (note effect of the /n/ in holding back the /d/), swept theatrically past. Can you add to these examples?

Why is dentalization poor? It gives speech a flat, dumpy sound. It retards speed. It often affects the pronunciation of /θ/ and /ð/. It is associated with a low social level. It may also suggest foreignism. Of course, it is only one of the many things that hamper good, clear speech. There are people who speak clearly and well without alveolar _t_'s, but they compensate in many ways: through firm emphasis, good inflectional patterns, unusually clear vowel sounds. Are your students sure they can do the same? If the students learn that they dentalize, either by observing themselves in a mirror or by being told so in the speech clinic, have them turn back to the beginning of this chapter and go through the initial drills once more.

The so-called blurred pronunciations of /tl/, /dl/, /tn/, /dn/, /tm/ and /dm/ in words like _little, middle, cotton, widen, bottom_, and _madam_ are somewhat more complicated. In these words the final vowel has disappeared and its function has been taken over by /l̩/, /n̩/ and /m̩/. Thus, although these words have only one vowel sound, they have two syllables, the final consonants being known as syllabic consonants, _i.e._, forming a syllable. The _t_'s and _d_'s have been absorbed and are not enunciated separately even in unaspirated manner, but take on the characteristic enunciation of the following consonant. Thus, in _little_ and _middle_ the /tl/ and /dl/ are emitted laterally; in _cotton_ and _widen_, as in _bottom_ and _madam_, they are emitted as alveolar nasals and labial nasals respectively. To practice, have students think of the pronunciation in slow motion, that is, take the proper position for /t/ or /d/ but not enunciate them. Have them hold

137

the position and add the /l/, /n/ or /m/, enunciating laterally or nasally, being certain that they do not move the tongue away from the gum ridge as they enunciate both sounds. In effect, both consonants are enunciated together. Ask them, "Who can hold the /t/ or /d/ for a full ten seconds before enunciating on the next sound?" Two rather ugly sidestepping mispronunciations sometimes develop in enunciating these sounds:

1. The substitution of a glottal stop for the /t/ or /d/ so that the words become lɪʔl and mɪʔl.
2. The addition of a vowel that does not belong there: lɪtəl and mɪdəl.

Clusters involving *t*'s and *d*'s are truly difficult and need special attention. The /dnt/, as in *couldn't, shouldn't, wouldn't, didn't, hadn't, needn't,* must be attacked assiduously, because their several mispronunciations are demeaning to good speakers. The problem consists of pronouncing three alveolar sounds one after the other. How can this be done? We are helped by the fact that the middle sound of the *dnt* is a nasal one. Using the slow-motion technique, have students take the *d* position and hold it. From this point on, the tip of the tongue should not leave the gum ridge until the end. Holding the /d/, have them say the /n/, and, still not moving the tongue, enunciate an aspirate /t/. Have students say the sound slowly several times, then faster, alone and then in phrases like:

couldn't say "yes"; *couldn't* say "no"

Make sure you have eliminated the following mispronunciations: kʊʔnt and kʊdmt. The clinician will be aware of modifications in pronunciation due to initial consonants of the following word in the same breath group, as in: "couldn't think," "shouldn't people."

The /sts/ cluster is perhaps the most difficult, because control is centered on a small alveolar spot. In order to achieve an easy and accurate triple cluster, be sure, first, that the /ts/ is sharp and clear. Try it in these words: *mitts, meats, cats, coats, wits, waits, boots, pits, flits, frets, thoughts, torts, darts, sits, sorts, sheets, chats, jets.* Even better, have students take slips of paper and place them before their mouths. Pretend that the words have two syllables, the last one being /ts/. Pronounce the first /s/ lightly; the /ts/ sharply enough to move the paper. The /sts/ should be thought of as having an imperceptible break between the /s/ and the /ts/. Try it that way in these words:

pests, bastes, mists, wastes, fasts, frosts, thirsts, thrusts, toasts, lists, nests, dusts, cysts, chests, jests, jousts, casts, coasts, ghost, hosts

Each student should now be able to demonstrate the difference between these word pairs;

pets – pests; bets – bests; mitts – mists; waits – wastes; fats – fasts; vets – vests; Tate's – tastes; sits – cysts; jets – jests; cats – casts; gets – guests; hats – hastes
pest – pests; beast – beasts; mist – mists; waste – wastes; fast – fasts; vest – vests; thirst – thirsts; toast – toasts; insist – insists; chest – chests; jest – jests; cost – costs; ghost – ghosts; host – hosts

The same general procedure can be used for other clusters:

/pts/ "crypts" or "crept sinuously"
/fts/ "shafts" or "soft sound"
/kts/ "expects" or "lacked sense"
/bds/ "robbed someone"
/mds/ "roomed singly"
/thds/ "bathed Saturday"

139

Another characteristic behavior of /t/ and /d/ affects pronunciation. It involves an interesting time element when these sounds precede a similar sound in the following word. The tongue takes its position for the first /t/ or /d/, holds the position for a fraction of a second (the time it would take to reach the position for the second /t/ or /d/), and then enunciates the second one. This is called incomplete plosion. You can hear or sense the difference in these phrase pairs:

Mount Tom – mount 'em
count down – count on
kid task – kid asks
fight decently – fight easily
sound did – sound it

The same time element is not present in medial spellings which represent a single sound: *matter, madder, butter, Buddy, writer, rider.*

$\boxed{\eta/\eta g}$ There are many occasions when the clinician is made aware of the lack of sophistication of a typical school group, but nowhere is this lack more evident than in their knowledge of phonetic concepts. How carefully then must the clinician tread in making the following presentation: What is the last sound in the word *"sing"*? No, not /g/, not /n/ but /ng/. Is it one sound or two? One sound in that word, but it can be two sounds elsewhere. Is it always spelled that way? No, the *ng* sound can be spelled *n* when followed by /k/, as in *ink,* or *include;* and *ngue* at the end of some words – *tongue, harangue,* and *meringue.* Be careful, however, for we are not now considering the soft sound of *ng* – the /ndʒ/ cluster, as in *change* or *engine,* nor its kissing cousin in the separate syllables of *ungrateful* and *inglorious,* where it is /ng/.

With that out of the way, the clinician may plunge into the *ng* rules for the "other" *ng* words, setting up a variable; namely,

140

that the same spelling is pronounced either as the single sound /ŋ/ or a double sound /ŋg/. Three rules control these pronunciations:

1. The *ng* is one sound /ŋ/ at the end of a word and in the clusters /ŋkθ/ and /ŋkθən/. For example, *sing, walking, length, lengthen.*°

2. It remains one sound /ŋ/ when the root word ending in *ng* adds a morpheme. For example, *hangs, hanger, hang-ing,, hangman, hangnail, hangover.*

This rule is so stringently applied that it perforce eliminates a word like *hangar* since airplanes are stored, not hung.

Some words will give the students difficulty because they appear to have a suffix but in reality do not, thus *hunger* is not composed of the morpheme *-er* added to the root meaning *hung* — and similarly for *single* or *singly.* In words like *English* or *language* there appears to be a legitimate morpheme, but it is not added to a known root word in *-ng.* The *ng* is, therefore, *not* a single sound in these words.

Place names, however, are included in rule two even though the root word is not recognizable. *Kingston* is still seen to be the king's town, but *Bingham, Binghamton,* and *Nottingham* must be assumed to have been someone's hamlet.

Include in this pronunciation the word *gingham* for any dark, etymological reason of your own.

Exceptions to rule two are the comparatives and superlatives *longer, longest, stronger, strongest, younger, young-est,* and the words *elongate, elongation,* and *diphthongal.* In these words the *ng* is pronounced /ŋg/. On the other

° The /k/ is a liaison sound only.

hand, the noun *longer* — one who longs — is not an exception to the rule.

3. In all other words where *ng* is medial, it is pronounced as the cluster /ŋg/; for example, *finger, hunger, linger.*

This is the traditional background of *ng* lessons. It does not, however, touch on the heart of the matter, which is this: The sound of /ŋ/ is one of the most beautiful liquid sounds in our speech, giving it carrying power.

- Adding an incorrect, unwanted click to it is both ugly and a foreignism. lɒŋg aɪlənd for lɒŋ aɪlənd
- Failing to pronounce a firm velar plosive in words that require it constitutes both a foreignism and substandard diction. sɪŋl for sɪŋgl
- Substituting /n/ for /ŋ/ is substandard. lenθ for leŋθ

The clinician's proper job at the school level, it appears to us, is to simplify the formal etymologic background and to check, improve, and make it possible for the students to control the two pronunciations /ŋ/ and /ŋg/.

DRILL I: *Objective:* To achieve a lengthened, singing final /ŋ/ sound without a click. If students have difficulty with this, advise them to move the tongue slightly forward when separating it from the velum.

ping – pang – pong; pring – prang – prong; bing – bang – bong; bring – brang – brung; ming – mang – among; wing – wang – wong; fing – fang – fong; fling – flang – flung; thing – thang – thong; ting – tang – tong; ding – dang – dong; sing – sang – song; sting – stang – stung; ching – chang – chong; jing – jang – jong; ling – lang – long; ring – rang – wrong; ying – yang – young; king – kang – kong; ging – gang – gong

142

DRILL II: *Objective:* To distinguish /n/ from /ŋ/.

pin – ping; been – Bing; Min – Ming; win – wing; Flynn – fling; thin – thing; tin – ting; tan – tang; ton – tongue; din –ding; done – dung; sin – sing; son – sung; chin – Ching; Chan – Chang; kin – king; gone – gong; Hun – hung; push in – pushing; see in – seeing; sit in – sitting; spy in – spying; run in – running; walk in – walking; think in – thinking; fall in – falling; step in – stepping; love in – loving

DRILL III. *Objective*: To maintain a singing /ŋ/ without a click even when followed by a vowel sound.

Long Island, long ago, sing along, song of India, sang out, going up, laughing out loud, riding a horse, mowing a lawn, typing a letter, washing a floor, cutting out a pattern

To the student: Make up a list describing a game, your day, or some activity using phrases like the above. Be sure that the *ng* is followed by a vowel sound. Example: Baseball: pitching one ball, missing a ball, catching a missed ball, running all bases, getting a homerun, catching a fly, hating umpires, watching our team, cheering it, etc.

Poets have long made use of this sound in building sound-sense images. Can you make up a sound picture like this one of a woman starting a car:

Rushing and scraping, tugging and scratching, turning and twisting, backing and braking, shrieking and stopping . . . but LOOKING? No.

Try an airplane taking off, or a ride in the subway, streets piled with autumn leaves, a motorcycle, waiting for the bell.

DRILL IV. *Objective:* To enunciate a singing /ŋ/ followed by a clear /g/. Practice first with a pause between them. A slight pause does exist because of the syllable separation between the /ŋ/ and the /g/.

bangle, bungle, Bangor, wangle, mingle, mangle, mongrel, mongoose, finger, fungus, tingle, tangle, dingle, dangle, single, singly, stronger, strongest, spangle, strangle, longer (adj), longest, languor, language, linger, lingering, shingle, jingle, jangle, jungle, younger, youngest, congregate, clangor, hangar, hunger, angle, England, English, Unguentine, wrangle

DRILL V. *Objective:* To enunciate a singing /ŋ/ followed by a clear /k/. These words have no connection with the above rules, but they have similar patterns of pronunciation.

ankle, inkling, increment, uncle, pink, Pinkerton, prank, plank, bank, banker, banking, bunker, blinker, blank, brink, wink, winking, mink, monk, flank, flunk, frank, thank, thanking, think, thinking, tank, tanker, tinkle, tinker, trunk, drink, drank, drunk, drinker, drinking, drunkard, link, cufflinks, lanky, rink, wrinkle, rankle, sink, sank, sunk, sinker, stink, sprinkle, shank, chink, hijinks, junk, canker, Younker, conquer, clink, clank, hanker, handkerchief

COGNATE CONFUSIONS

A cognate pair consists of two consonants articulated in the same place and enunciated in the same way, the only difference between them being that one is voiced, the other voiceless. A cognate confusion consists of the substitution of a sound for its cognate. Thus, any of the nine voiceless-voiced pairs of consonants are open to this error.

Error	Mispronunciation	Characteristic of
p/b	b̥ɔɪz goʊ b̥eɪðɪŋ * "boys go bathing"	Germanic background.
b/p	b̩eɪ fə ðə b̩ɪlz † "pay for the pills"	Germanic background.
w/ʍ	Discussed in this chapter.	
ʍ/w	Rare.	
f/v	v̥erɪ laɪylɪ * "very lively"	Germanic background.
v/f	Rare.	
θ/ð	briθ wiθ dɪfɪkəltɪ "breathe with difficulty"	Generally due to ignorance.
ð/θ	ðæŋks fɚ evrɪðɪŋ "thanks for everything"	Germanic background. Also the result of dentalization.
t/d	hɪz d̥ɔtə ɪz gud̥ "his daughter is good"	Germanic, Yiddish, Italian, or Scandinavian background.
d/t	Discussed in this chapter.	Probably dentalization.
s/z	ʍɒt wəs hɪs risn "what was his reason"	Spanish or Germanic background. Greatly influenced by parallel structures in mother tongue.
z/s	Rare.	
ʃ/ʒ	See Drill I below.	Same as for s/z.

* Partial unvoicing of the voiced consonant, represented by o under the consonant.
† Unaspirated.

ERROR	MISPRONUNCIATION	CHARACTERISTIC OF
ʒ/ʃ	Rare.	
tʃ/dʒ	kɒlɪdʒ bɔɪz læŋgwɪdʒ * "college boys' language"	A fairly common unvoicing characteristic of substandard speech. Germanic influence.
dʒ/tʃ	Rare.	
k/g	ɪŋgrɪd ɪz ə g̊ʊd g̊ɝl	Scandinavian background.
g/k	Rare.	

Medial sibilant voicings are particularly difficult for Spanish speakers, especially when spelled with s.

DRILL I. *Objective:* To distinguish the spelling s from the pronunciations /z/ and /ʒ/.

reason, pleasing, raisin, rising, raising, losing, spasm, because, poison, vision, precision, illusion, confusion, occasion, pleasure, measure, appeasing

A confusion having its origin in a misinterpretation of English orthography by students of Spanish origin is the substitution of /dʒ/ for /j/. Ear training and an explanation of the kinesthesia should precede the drill.

DRILL II: Distinguish between initial /dʒ/ and /j/.

jot – yacht; Jack – yak; jail – Yale; jam – yam; jokers – yogurt; Jap – yap; jarred – yard; jaw – yaw; jaundice – yawn; jay – yea; jeer – year; jell – yell; Jello – yellow; jet – yet; Jew – you; jest – yes; joke – yolk; jowl – yowl; John – yon; gesture – yes to her; journey – yearning.

PRACTICE BLANK: CONSONANT CHART							
MANNER OF EMISSION	PLACE OF ARTICULATION						
Nasal							
Plosive							
Fricative							
Fricative Blends							
Lateral							
	1	2	3	4	5	6	7

The clinician should supply each student with a copy of the consonant chart like the one above. Then, in conjunction with his students, he should elicit the correct placement of the consonants (or those he wishes to concentrate on). In this way, the facts of articulation will be better understood and the chart itself will have greater significance. For student use, the positions may be labeled as follows:

1. lip to lip
2. lower lip to upper teeth
3. tip of tongue to teeth
4. tip of tongue to gum ridge

5. mid tongue to hard palate
6. back of tongue to palate
7. throat (glottis)

IX

English as a Second Language

In many urban and suburban communities there has been a growing need for special classes for students coming from other countries with not enough knowledge of English to pursue successfully a regular school program on any level. In New York City, in 1965, for example, there were 190,000 students from sixty different countries. Great effort and liberal allotments in the form of state, local, and federal grants have been applied to provide programs for these young people. Bilingual counselors, selected teachers, small classes, specially devised instructional material and texts, and classes in summer schools are offered. The speech clinic provides an important part of their training, and is, in fact, the key class during the early period of their adjustment.

The question may be asked: Since many texts for the teaching of English as a foreign language also emphasize an aural-oral approach, what is the difference between the English classes (called "basic," "orientation," "transition," "TESOL" [Teaching of English to Speakers of Other Languages], and "special")

148

and the speech clinic? The answer is: The major activity of all speech clinics is speaking practice. Nowhere is this truism more applicable than with students in a speech class for those learning English as a second language. If the students know only three words, they must practice speaking these words. "Hello," "How are you?," "My name is —," "I live at —," "Good-bye," and "Thank you" are as difficult for the beginner and as worthy of drill as are more involved structures later in the course. A second truism that points up the difference between English classes and speech clinics is that language is not learned passively. Insofar as possible, each student must himself speak the words and structures being studied. This is what the speech clinician must make crystal clear at the beginning of the term. The basic activity of the speech clinic is oral, and to maintain it takes considerable management on the part of the clinician. But first of all it takes dedication to this point of view. If a child is shy or reluctant to come before the class — understandable where the language for communication is limited — the clinician may as a last resort accept a form of substitute participation, such as facing the group from the seat or answering questions put by the teacher until the child is willing or able to participate with the group. Thirdly, the speech clinic differs from the English class in that it devotes considerable time to drill. Drills in unison, drills with individual children, saturation drills, contrastive drills, substitution and transformation drills, and "chain" techniques. Fourth, the speech clinic sets up experiences in ear training and listening. These experiences may be simply conceived or may involve the use of a language laboratory. (See suggested drills at the end of this chapter.) Fifth, the speech clinic provides, when the students are ready for it, experiences in the speech arts such as role playing and dramatizations. Sixth, from the beginning, students are introduced to phonemic concepts, the clinician using / / for sounds.

Students in the speech clinic for English as a second language are usually divided into three groups according to the

Scale for Rating Pupils' Ability to Speak English (Appendix D): those with very little or no facility in speaking English; those with a basic vocabulary and control over simple language structures; and those assigned to regular English classes who speak with a marked foreign accent. Three types of classes are accordingly provided: the basic, the advanced, and the foreign accent clinic. All three will be discussed and described. These disadvantaged students, especially those of the first group, will continue to be disadvantaged until they can adequately speak the English language in their communities, the first of which is the school community.

Ideally, students in the first two groups should be programmed to have a period of English followed later in the day by a period of speech. Many schools attempt to do this, but there are several factors militating against them. It is hard to keep the class together as a unit because of the current emphasis on individual rather than block programming. Thus, Juan may be more interested in electric shop than in woodworking, to which others in the group are scheduled. In most schools his individual preference will take priority. The girls as a group may be assigned to sewing, while Nubia, talented in painting, will have her program arranged to take that special class. Secondly, there is great diversity among the many students entering our schools. We find students who have had little training in reading and writing their native language and limited experience in community and family situations common to urban living, as well as students who not only read and write their mother tongue excellently, but who have had a good start in English. Thirdly, the fact that students are permitted to register in school throughout the term means that any airtight organization set up at the beginning of the term is liable to undergo great changes in registration within a month or two. We are back again to a familiar situation. The speech clinician will have to be prepared to teach a group that may have been set up as a homogeneous group but is in fact no longer that. As before, therefore, it becomes his obligation to find the level of achievement of each student. The sooner he discovers with whom he is working the more meaningful he can make the clinic.

THE BASIC SPEECH CLINIC

Let us assume that the ideal situation exists and that the speech clinic as a unit follows the English class. The students' work in English can then be integrated and reinforced by the speech class. The clinician will provide further drills for vocabulary and language structures already taught, and set up simulated life situations for their use. The speech clinician will, furthermore, set up a course based on the sounds of English as they appear in these lessons; he will provide special lessons on problems of particular difficulty for the students, such as cognate or other consonant confusions, pronunciation of the final -ed in words like *napped, nabbed,* and *needed;* homonyms; words with silent letters, etc. He will include as often as possible ear training on sounds, especially vowels that are similar but not alike. (See the contrastive drills in Chapter VII.)

A typical speech lesson following an English period devoted to telling time might take the following form. (A large clock with movable hands — available commercially but easily made by the clinician — is a helpful visual device to reinforce the lesson.)

1. (Once over lightly): Good morning. What was the subject of your lesson today in English? [He knows, but do they?] Telling time. Good. What was it, Bianca? Can you tell time, Edgar? Does your mother tell time? [Laughter. Mother tell(s) time in Spanish . . . but the needed change in the verb has been made.] Who tells time in your family? Do both you and your sister tell time? [Yes, they both tell time.]

2. (Intensive group and individual practice): Clinician uses flash cards, slowly at first, and then faster. [He may end with a challenge to anyone who wants to read five cards "quickly."] One o'clock, six o'clock, twelve o'clock, five o'clock, half-past

. . . a quarter past . . . a quarter to . . . ten [minutes] past . . . ten to . . . 2:20, 4:30.

3. (Drill on an important sound): We must be very clear when we tell time. Let us look at one sound that can help us. What sound is the same in "ten" and "two"? [There is a short presentation of aspirate /t/, followed by group and individual drill of the sound in isolation and in syllables, ending with the flash cards for 1:10, 2:10, 3:10, 12:50 [twelve-fifty or ten to one] 1:50, 2:50, etc. The teacher comments liberally "good," "fine," "very good," "uh-uh" – a shake of the head – "better."

4. (A short dictation, which is a fine way to evaluate what the students hear): A rule for spelling. We know that spelling in English is not very phonetic. Here is a bad spelling with a good rule. What sounds does the *qu* really make in the word *quarter?* [Elicit /kw/.] That is our rule. Write: The spelling *qu* is always pronounced /kw/. Who can give me another word spelled with *qu?* [Question, quiet, inquire.]

5. (Practice in free conversation): What do you do at seven o'clock in the morning? [Most of the class answers, beginning "At seven o'clock, I . . ."]

6. (For homework): Write your diary for today or for any other day you wish, even Sunday. Have at least five things that you do, beginning with a time phrase. Be prepared to read it in class.

The speech lesson outlined above is a logical follow-up of the original presentation lesson in the English class. The lesson involved some twenty vocabulary words (time, day, night, clock, watch, watchband, face, long hand, short hand, hour(s), minute(s), second(s), twenty-four, eight, twelve, sixty, morning, evening, noon, midnight); structure patterns for questions and answers; idioms like "Every hour on the hour"; and the introduction of time concepts. You as the speech clinician worked toward making these concepts automatic and easier; you worked for clarity; you extended the application of the learned vocabulary; and you made sure that each student spoke as often as possible. The next session will be devoted to hearing the diaries read, thus providing individual practice and group listening. The English class may have been assigned a test for that day.

If, however, the work of the speech clinic and the English class is not integrated, it may be necessary for the speech clinician to assume part of the work of an English class and introduce units of vocabulary, setting up situations in which the vocabulary can be used as well as doing the proper work of a speech class.

The unit plan of work is especially serviceable here. Let us assume that it is the beginning of the term and that the group has little or no facility in the use of English — that is, that they are rated E or F on the Scale for Rating Pupils' Ability. What is appropriate vocabulary for this group, new to the school, to the community, to the language, and, in many cases, to a way of life? We suggest that it is a vocabulary suited to their immediate needs and immediate community — the school. Twenty units, consisting of a vocabulary of approximately twenty words each, based on areas of school life can constitute the greater part of the term's work. Such a vocabulary will not only be basically usable, but will help considerably with their orientation to the school. The basic course will then provide a meaningful vocabulary of some 900 words. Four hundred of these will be "use" words, 300 "function" words — pronouns, verbs, verb forms, adjectives, adverbs and prepositions — and the rest will be culled from drills and free association. It is recommended that the clinician consult a professional list such as the Thorndike-Lorge Word Frequency List when composing drills. With encouragement, the students will bring in unfamiliar words that they have not understood in other classes. We once spent five fruitful minutes unwinding a misconception about "hem" and "cuff." Another source of experience vocabulary is the "sound-alikes." These are not necessarily homonyms. Carlos' mother was asked at the clinic if her finger felt "numb." "But she have a finger. Why they ask?" inquired Carlos. He was thinking of the only word he knew with "that" sound — "none."

153

Developing a Unit

What is meant by developing a unit? Let us take one used early in the term [1] — "My program card" — and see what it is that we actually do. A unit should consist of at least three lessons: a presentation, review and drill, and free conversation. The vocabulary for "My program card" consisted of the following words: program card,[2] period(s), subject class(es), names of the specific subjects taken by the class, subject teacher, homeroom teacher, guidance counselor, health education, assembly seat, gymnasium (gym), hygiene, lunch period, cafeteria, lunch token, early dismissal, locker number. (The list should conform to actual terminology, which varies from school to school. The clinician can easily make his own list.)

The first period was spent in a rote reading of the vocabulary and in spelling dictation. The clinician should provide himself with an enlarged version of a program card — by using an overhead projector, copying one onto a large cardboard with a felt pen, or reproducing one on the board. The students will have their own program cards on their desks. The clinician points to, reads, and explains each item on the card and the class repeats it. Individual students are requested to repeat a word from time to time. It is very important that the clinician acknowledge the performance of his students. Encouragement is a useful device; conversely, silence can provide a negative commentary. Five or ten words should be adequate for dictation, especially if the

[1] The following units were tested in use: (1) Who are you? I am —, (2) My program card, (3) Eating in the school cafeteria, (4) We go to assembly, (5) A visit to the first floor, (6) Floorplan of the first (second, third) floor, (7) I live near (far from) the school, (8) People in the school (principal, patrol monitors, etc.), (9) I must leave school early today, (10) How to borrow a book from the school library, (11) I talk with my guidance counselor, (12) My report card, (13) An important holiday, (14) What I bring to school (notebook, textbooks, etc.), (15) My new friends, (16) Is this school different from the one in —, (17) How to study; Planning my program for next term, (18) After school I do many things, (19) My family, (20) My favorite sport.
[2] Two words form a unit of meaning.

clinician points out a few salient features such as the long *o* in *home* and in *token;* soft and hard *g*'s in *gym* and *guidance.*

The second period will require flash cards prepared in advance with a word or a portion of the program card pictured on them. These are then held up for affirmative responses first, followed by negative responses, and then mixed ones. The group must be conditioned early to use the key words in their answers and to answer in complete sentences, even though, we acknowledge, that is not a natural procedure. Your drill will take this pattern: "Is this a subject class?" "Yes, it is a subject class." "No, it is not a subject class." "No, it is not, it is a homeroom class." Other drills that may be used on this day or subsequently are:

FREE ANSWERS: The vocabulary is used in questions such as "Do you go to gym every day?" "Have you five subject classes on your program card?" "Who is your guidance counselor?" "What is your locker number?" "What is your lunch period?" "Who is your class teacher?"

USE OF THE VOCABULARY IN CHAIN TECHNIQUE: A question is set by the teacher and practiced by the class as a whole. The first student addresses it to the pupil behind him: "Is Spanish [gym, English, woodshop] your best subject?" The second pupil answers: "Yes [or no], Spanish is [or isn't] my best subject." The second student then turns and asks the pupil behind him a similar question: "Is gym your best subject?" although he is free to repeat the same question. This goes on until all have asked and answered a question. The last student closes the chain by addressing his question to the first.

SUBSTITUTION DRILLS: The teacher sets up a starting sentence such as "The first period I go to the gymnasium [to gym]." He then suggests single-unit alternates which the pupil called on must fit into the sentence by substituting them for something there. Thus:

Teacher offers:	*Sentence becomes:*
second	The *second* period I go to the gymnasium.
study hall	The second period I go to the *study hall.*
after lunch	*After lunch* I go to the study hall.
he	After lunch *he* goes to the study hall.
Maria	After lunch Maria goes to the study hall.
Maria and I	After lunch *Maria and I* go to the study hall.
today	*Today* Maria and I go to the study hall.
no one	Today *no one* goes to the study hall.
the whole class	Today *the whole class* goes to the study hall.
the language laboratory	Today the whole class goes to the language laboratory.

The final exercise in a unit must be free and original oral composition, however simple. As soon as possible, the clinician may introduce the concept of a general, or topic, sentence and a concluding remark. The following is an adequate "speech" given by a student in the first month of the class. All the students spoke on the topic, a few responding to questions.

> My program card is very good. I like it very much. I have three subjects before lunch: sewing, world geography, and English. After lunch I have Spanish. It is my best subject. Then I have speech. The seventh period I have gym. Then I go home. I have early dismissal because I help my father in the store.

Much supplementary and illustrative material is needed in this clinic. Pictures are perhaps most useful, forming, as they do, a communicative bridge. Many teachers have been challenged to make their own collections — from magazines, advertisements, catalogues. These are effective if they are large enough or if they can be reproduced. Action pictures are often available from motion picture companies and are useful for role playing and imaginative "tellings." High-quality records and tapes on the sounds of English are also available. The use of a language laboratory is of great benefit, although frequently the clinician must make his own tapes. (Drills for such tapes can be found in Chapters VII and VIII.)

The experienced and gifted clinician will seek to maintain a balance in his lessons between a welcome repetitiveness and new and varied elements. From the units suggested it is easy to progress, if time allows, to others related to the students' needs outside of school. In making a choice of topics we are well advised by Booker T. Washington to "set down our buckets where we are." Here is a tested list. Note that the topics are specific and personal:

My apartment; The kitchen; The bedroom; The living room; The bathroom; Taking a bus; Taking the subway; Taking an airplane; Telling time; The supermarket; I buy some groceries; I buy some fruit and vegetables; I buy some meat; I go to the bakery; What is the weather?; I buy a pair of shoes; I buy a dress (suit); I eat in a restaurant; I go to the post office; The USA (map study); A holiday; The beauty parlor; The automobile; Packing a suitcase.

In addition to developing a basic vocabulary of from fifteen to twenty words, each unit should introduce several "use" words. Thus, the units on rooms can distinguish between *in, on, over,* and *under.* The linoleum is *on* the floor, but the dishes are *in* the dish closet. There is a picture *over* the sofa and a rug *under* it. Similarly, as you enter the apartment there is a room *on the right,* another *on the left.* One takes a bus *every day,* the subway *often,* and an airplane *sometimes.* If such idioms do not suggest themselves out of the day-to-day needs of the students, the clinician

157

can find a good assortment in the paperback *Essential Idioms in English* [3] by R. J. Dixson.

It is good pedagogy to compare what you planned the students should learn for the first term and what, indeed, they have learned. It may be far more than you expected. It is also good pedagogy to recognize the need for repetition and to remember that language is not so much learned as it is *attached* — to cultural roots that are there, to needs, and to experiences.

The clinician should also bear in mind the point of view so well stated in the *Staff Bulletin* Special Supplement published by the New York City Public Schools commenting on the School Volunteer Program,[4] a project in which trained volunteers worked with groups of eight to ten children on conversational English:

> These children already have a first language which is natural and important to them. Their culture, their heritage and their language are all intimately related, and respect for their first language by the volunteer implies respect for the children as individuals. English constitutes no improvement over the children's native language. It is merely a tool they must have if they are to be educated in our schools.

THE ADVANCED SPEECH CLINIC

Your students have been in the school for a semester or for a year. They feel quite adequate in getting about the school. They are disdainful of the newcomers who don't know what a homeroom class is and must be reminded that it was only a short while ago that they were in the same position. They bounce into the speech clinic trying out their picked-up expressions on the teacher — "How's every little thing?" "Okay." "Be seein' you." They wonder what more you can teach them. There is a great

---

[3] R. J. Dixson, *Essential Idioms in English* (New York, Regents, 1951).
[4] The project, which had 130 volunteers at the end of five years, was highly successful. Basic vocabulary was taught by using pictures and miniature objects.

temptation for you, knowing how imperfect their language is and how fragile their hold on basic vocabulary, to stay with the simple forms "until they are learned." We do not believe that this is a suitable dynamic for language learning. The clinician must assume the student's readiness to advance if he passed the basic course. From the start he will let the students feel that new and more extensive experiences will be theirs. We have seen too many classes that never went beyond repetitions of certain well-defined and familiar basic situations.

On the other hand, frequent review is in order, geared to freer communication situations. The following problems make use of known vocabulary:

- You have come home from the first day of school. You have just received your new program card. Call your friend on the telephone and compare programs.
- You are late to school because of an emergency at home. Explain this to your teacher.
- A student newly arrived from Puerto Rico asks you where the gym is. Tell her how to get there. Let us know from what place you are giving the directions.
- You enjoy the game of soccer and would like to play. Ask one of the boys about it.

One problem that will undoubtedly arise in relation to the advanced speech clinic is the old one of homogeneity. If necessary, you will be able to assimilate into the class a new entrant to the school who has some background and experience in English. You should not have to accept a student who should really be in the basic class. Make every effort to place him there. You may be faced with the final plaintive argument: "Isn't it better for him to have the wrong class than none at all?" A teacher is a many-splendored martyr and may accede to the force if not to the validity of the argument, but there is, we suggest, an option open to the administrator; namely, private or small group practice for the few who cannot be fitted into the proper clinic. These groups can be supervised by paid aides or qualified students.

What are the concentrations of the advanced clinic? They are:

1. Drill on basic structures and idioms of the language.
2. Drill on the sounds of English, including ear-training exercises.
3. Reading out loud; phrasing and intonation.
4. Free conversation and role playing.

The clinician is advised to select one or several reading texts, and perhaps a workbook, on the basis of the group's interest and ability.

Let us now consider idioms and structures. By consulting the school's or the English department's outline of the course of study, or a standard grammar, the clinician can easily choose a dozen to begin with and then expand the list as needs develop. In this way he should be able to cover some three hundred grammatical structures or idioms during a semester. Here is an introductory dozen, chosen arbitrarily:

1. Questions beginning with *do, does,* and *did.*
2. Questions beginning with *where* and *when.*
3. Questions beginning with *who* and *whose.*
4. *Who* as a relative pronoun.
5. *Which* and *that* as relative pronouns.
6. Pronouns in the nominative.
7. Matching pronouns to a possessive antecedent.
8. Sentences beginning *There is* and *There are.*
9. Questions beginning *Is there* and *Are there.*
10. Idiomatic use of *at home* and *home.*
11. Change of the verb in the third person singular of the present tense.
12. Idiomatic expressions like *turn on* and *turn off.*

If the speech clinician does not have facility in the languages needed for the group, it is suggested that he learn key grammatical and procedural words as an aid to teaching. Language teachers, advanced students, and language dictionaries can help him do this. The main block of time in the speech clinic is, as always, to be spent on oral drill and practice speaking. A fifteen-minute session on the first unit above may take this form:

1. The students find a conjugation on the blackboard and copy it when they arrive: I do, You do, He does, We do, etc. (Same for *did*.)

2. Unison repetition. Clinician offers a variety of subjects — I, They, Marie, His mother, etc. — in a substitution drill.

3. Clinician illustrates a conversion from declarative to interrogative: Marie goes to school. Does Marie go to school? He then reads prepared sentences, inviting conversions. Have conversions all begin with *do*, then *does* and *did*. Afterward scramble them. A group response — even if a bit noisy — followed by individual repetitions or variants is good and efficient drill.

4. Pair off students, one to make a statement about himself, the other to convert it into a question. If fun is part of your classroom, mount a mask on a stick and let the "gossip" make a third conversation, thus:

    Student 1: "I go to church on Sunday."
    Student 2: "Does he go to church on Sunday?"
    Gossip: "He goes to church on Sunday!"

There will be a great deal of pattern work of this nature during the term, so that no unit should be longer than the above, which leaves a second half-period for activities of a different type — reading or conversing or taping or ear training.

One type of exercise popular with students is called "Many Questions." Here are some typical sequences:

1. Where is the dictionary? Is it there now? Was it there yesterday? Who put it there? Did you see him put it there? Is it a big book? Is it very heavy? Is it useful? Do you use it? When do you use it?

2. Does your family have a car? Do you want to drive? Are you a driver? Why not? Do you sit in front or in back? When must you stop the automobile? Did you visit someone? What does the driver do with the wheel? What does he do with the brake? How many people can sit in your car?

3. How often do you go shopping? Who shops for food? Do you help? Do you go to small stores or to the supermarket? What do you like to choose? Do you have many packages? Who carries the packages? Are they heavy? Where do you pay? Is the store far from your home?

A variation on having one student answer the sequence is to have a small team of three or four, all of whom must answer the questions fairly rapidly.

Another exercise is called "Everyone works hard" — or use any other similar variation. The clinician supplies the topic sentence while the student (or students) answers, using a correct pronoun as subject.

Clinician	Students
My sister is a student.	She works hard.
My mother is a housewife.	She works hard.
His father is a plumber.	He works hard.
Nixon is president.	He works hard.
The soccer team practices every day.	They work hard.
I try to teach all the students.	You work hard.
The old car climbs the hill.	It works hard.

In this way, a great many essential grammatical structures

and concepts can be presented orally. Although you will not present vocabulary units formally this term, encourage students to gather and develop vocabulary on their own.

A second concentration is on the sounds of English as they affect the acquisition of the language. Students must listen to, and discriminate between, sounds; they must begin to learn their physical characteristics so that they can form them; they must learn to associate spelling normalities with sounds, and learn, too, some anomalies of spelling; they must practice patterns of intonation and some of the uses of inflection. In reading they must become aware of word groupings and the logical phrasing of thoughts, and should begin to understand the concept of emphasis. And, finally, they must continue to express themselves in conversations, presentations, informal discussions — first in a limited way and then more fully.

What should be the clinician's orientation in maintaining a high accomplishment level for this group? We say, think *drill*, think *chorusing*, think *responsive reading*. Minimize formal, inductive presentations. There will be some, of course, but limit them to one specific aspect and keep them short. Do not worry overmuch about the level of sophistication of the lessons, provided you think of your students as young adults and treat them accordingly. People learning a language trim back their sophistication — they adopt a "willing suspension" of it. On the other hand, the clinician may, by reserving a few minutes at the end of the period for free discussion on issues that concern students at their level, restore their self-image.

THE FOREIGN ACCENT CLINIC

Here is the aristocrat of the language sequence — the top clinic of its kind. All students in this group have qualified for and are presently registered in regular English classes. A fine bond has developed between these students and the Speech Department. The clinicians are involved in the minutiae of their

163

lives in school: Did Juan get the class in stagecraft that he wanted? Good. We expect him to bring in many new words. Elvira is wearing the outfit she made for herself in sewing. What a good fit it is! Carlos would like to help in the speech office. A fine idea!

The euphoria we describe has been earned through good clinical practice on two levels. It is now incumbent upon us to provide a third level of achievement whose main characteristics will be self-understanding and self-responsibility. The term should start with a language evaluation for each student followed by a conference with each. The student must share in the process of evaluating his speech — its strengths and weaknesses — and help determine his primary and secondary goals for achievement. A very satisfactory way of doing this is to have each student record his reading of a suitable paragraph on tape. Within a month, have him reread the same paragraph and play both tapes back for him. In this way a progress evaluation can be made.

The work of the term in general should include the following, in addition to the personal goals of the students:

- a review of all the sounds of the English language, utilizing the vowel scale and consonant chart
- comparative drills on nodes of difficulty
- work with intonation and inflection patterns
- listening and ear training sessions
- interpretive, choral, and conversational readings
- role playing and free discussion

Students in clinic groups at this level often have individual needs or interests — one group wished to read newspapers to help them with their history, another to practice "giving proofs," which they found hard to do orally in mathematics. One student wanted to "try out" his book report. These are all legitimate and worthwhile areas for exploration.

In working with the vowel scales and consonant chart, the

clinician should emphasize the significance of the tongue positions and the differences in articulation and emissions rather than insist on the learning of phonetic symbols. When a sound has been discussed, placing the symbol in its proper place on the chart is not the responsibility of the clinician but of the student. It should be the last step in a many-faceted approach to the sound.

Sample Reading Selection for Taping

The Christmas vacation will soon be here. There are eleven days to the holiday this year, and I am going to spend all of them with my family in Puerto Rico. Immediately after school, my uncle will take my mother, my sister, and me to the airport. In the meantime, I will be very busy washing clothes, buying presents, and packing. Soon Thursday will be here, then "Good-bye books" I'll say. My cousin is going with us; we already have our tickets. We generally arrive quite early at the airport, listen for the announcement of our flight, and then board the plane. Once I fasten my seat belt, hear the noise of the engine, and experience the magic moment when we are airborne, the holiday has begun. At San Juan someone from the family will meet us when we arrive. It is a great occasion for all.

EAR-TRAINING DRILL: Provide each student with a copy of the drill. Avoid discussion of word meanings; this may be done later. *Instructions to students:* Put a circle around the word that has the sound asked for by your teacher. Remember that spelling may be unphonetic. Each line will be read twice.

Sound	Words	Mark
1. /b/	comb, potato, Havana, rob	————
2. /d/	ripped, ribbed, roped, rocked	————
3. /b/	thumb, plumber, able, doubt	————

Sound	Words	Mark
4. no /t/	listen, two, ten, asked	_____
5. /t/	Christmas, bouquet, hoped, often	_____
6. /l/	palm, half, let, chalk	_____
7. long ō /oʊ/	won, want, won't, one	_____
8. no long vowel	east, eat, even, eleven	_____
9. long ō /oʊ/	bond, bun, cross, sew	_____
10. /æ/	age, page, same, sad	_____
11. no /eɪ/	says, saying, say, save	_____
12. /æ/	sell, said, says, Sam	_____

NOTE: The above drill represents difficulties common in the FA (foreign accent) group. Point out that Spanish is həb̞ɑnə and palmə.

DRILL: Tongue placement for /p/ /θ/ /t/ /f/. Students are to use hand mirrors and watch differences in lip-tongue positions.

pie, thigh, tie, fie — pay, they, take, fake — pill, thrill, till, fill — plum, thumb, ton, fun — pause, thought, taught, fought — pear, there, tear, fare — pour, thaw, tore, for — peer, theater, teardrop, fear

COMPARATIVE DRILLS:

i ɪ e bean, been, bent — seek, sick, second — knee, knit, net — tease, 'tis, test — fleas, flick, phlegm — key, kid, Ked — crease, Chris, crest — leak, lick, lectern

æ ɑ pad, par — bad, bar — Sam, psalm — lamb, alarm — marry, mark — tan, tarnish — pack, park — am, arm — cat, cart — add, art — camera, calm — hat, heart — stand, star

166

$\boxed{\text{aɪ ɪ}}$ pride, pretty — prime, prim — time, trim — ice, is — Lysol, Listerine — sight, sit — like, lick — dime, dim — bite, bit — light, lit — flight, flit — cry, crib — mind, mint — sign, sin

$\boxed{\text{i u ɔ}}$ see, sue, saw — fleet, flute, flaw — cheese, chews, jaws — tree, true, trough — she, shoe, Shaw — deed, do, door — bead, boot, bore

$\boxed{\text{ɒ oʊ}}$ sock, soak — flock, float — chop, chose — drop, drove — cop, cope — job, Job — fond, phone — prosody, prose — Mott, mote — rock, wrote — Jock, joke — shock, showed

$\boxed{\text{e æ}}$ bet, bat — lend, land — wreck, wrack — head, had — send, sand — set, sat — pet, pat — prep, Pratt — fleck, flat — settle, saddle — shed, shad — Chet, chat — gem, jam

$\boxed{\text{ɛɚ ɝ ɔ̆}}$ where, were, wore — share, shirt, shore — hair, her, horse — pair, purr, pore — bear, burr, bore — care, curl, core — fair, fur, four — Sarah, certain, sore

$\boxed{\text{æ ɒ oʊ}}$ black, block, bloke — ax, ox, oaks — pat, pot, post — cat, cot, coat — gas, got, goat — grass, grotto, groat — rat, rot, wrote — crack, crock, croak — pack, pocket, poke

X

Anatomy and Physiology

———◆———

Students probably know a great deal more about the anatomy and physiology of their speech "computers" than they have ever put into words. We assume that every experienced as well as newly appointed teacher in the field of speech and language disorders possesses, as part of his training for this area, a good background knowledge of the anatomy and physiology of the speech organs. Students should also understand the basic processes of the formation of sounds in language and should know the basic vocabulary that pertains to the production of speech in order to be able to discuss the subject. It is not necessary for the student to learn in detail all that the clinician knows, but he should understand:

- the overlaid functions of the speech organs
- the complexity of producing even a single sound
- the five processes involved in sound production
- the control of breathing

* the names given to the organs of articulation and their functions

WHAT IS A SPEECH SOUND?

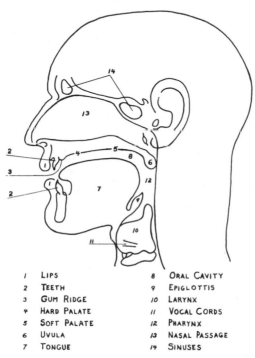

1	LIPS	*8*	ORAL CAVITY
2	TEETH	*9*	EPIGLOTTIS
3	GUM RIDGE	*10*	LARYNX
4	HARD PALATE	*11*	VOCAL CORDS
5	SOFT PALATE	*12*	PHARYNX
6	UVULA	*13*	NASAL PASSAGE
7	TONGUE	*14*	SINUSES

Your students have just entered the room and you call them by name. Each one answers "Here." Simple? No — complex! Ask the students to think of it in slow motion: their brain signals "That's me" (auditory feedback), and their speech "computer," which is constantly plugged into its "current" — air — in consequence directs some of the air power upward under pressure. As the air moves upward through the windpipe and voice box (larynx) the vocal cords remain separated because /h/, a voiceless consonant, does not require their vibration. Immediately

afterward, however, they approximate for /ɪɚ/, a voiced diphthong, which does. In the mouth, the tongue, the most mobile
of the "computer" parts, shapes the air column one way for the
/h/ (articulation), and another for /ɪɚ/. For /h/ it directs the air
through a narrow palatal opening [1] by bunching its midpoint
toward the front roof (palate) of the mouth; for the /ɪɚ/ the
air pours out through a much wider opening, the mid-tongue
lower and more relaxed. At the instant of their formation, the
sounds are reinforced in a very personal way by the air chambers
(resonating cavities) of the throat, mouth, and head. The sounds
then proceed out of the mouth (enunciation) to the listener over
sound waves. The whole process has taken a second!

The Production of Sound

There are five aspects to the production of language sounds:

1. An Initiator: The brain and nerve pathways. (Man makes
   sound for a purpose.)
2. A Motor: Air-control mechanisms — muscles of the abdomen and ribs, the diaphragm, the lungs branching into
   the windpipe. (The source of energy.)
3. A Vibrator: Vocal folds housed in the larynx. (Most
   sounds use voice — the air in vibration.)
4. Articulators: Tongue, teeth, inner gum ridges, especially
   the upper one, hard and soft palate ending in the pendu-
   lous uvula. (To form sounds into vowels and consonants.)
5. Resonators: Air chambers of the larynx, throat (pharynx),
   mouth, nasal passage, and possibly the sinuses. (The sound
   is amplified.)

The student should study a diagram of the speech mechanism — his computer — closely, noting the relation of the parts.
When he has done so, let him trace the outline and see if he

---

[1] /h/ is normally a glottal fricative; here it has been palatalized because of
assimilation.

can label each numbered part. He should understand that all of these structures are exceedingly more complex than presented here, but for classroom purposes these descriptions are sufficient.

We have briefly summarized below the pertinent information for those teachers and clinicians who may wish to refresh their knowledge in this area.[2]

The Respiratory System

The lungs are the essential organs of respiration and are located in the thoracic cavity. They are composed of passive,

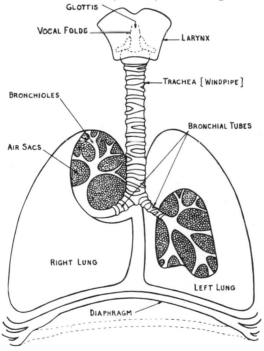

spongy, elastic material divided into lobes — two in the left lung, three in the right. The trachea, or windpipe, divides at its lower

[2] There are numerous books on the anatomy and physiology of speech; some are included in the Selected Bibliography.

end and passes one bronchial branch into each lung. These bronchi then divide into bronchioles and finally into alveoli, or air sacs. The bases of the lungs rest upon the diaphragm. Lung capacity varies with each individual.

Air is alternately inhaled and exhaled approximately sixteen times each minute. Inhalation occurs when the capacity of the thoracic cavity is increased; enlargement of this cavity creates a partial vacuum in the air sacs within the lungs and atmospheric pressure forces air into this partial vacuum. Exhalation (in speech, the vocal bands are set into vibration by exhaled breath from the lungs) occurs when the thoracic musculature and lung tissue resume their passive state, or when the dimensions of the thorax are voluntarily decreased by contraction of the surrounding musculature. When the latter is done, there is a more forcible expulsion of breath.

Inhalation, as described above, requires increase in the dimensions of the thoracic cavity, the framework of which articulates freely enough to permit sufficient changes in the volume. The lateral dimensions of the thoracic cavity are increased by the upward and outward movement of the ribs and a slight forward movement of the sternum. The muscles that raise and expand the ribs are located anteriorly, posteriorly, and laterally in homologous pairs.

The diaphragm is a broad, double-dome-shaped muscle extending across the base of the thoracic cavity. The floor of the thorax is lowered when the diaphragmatic musculature contracts, and the capacity of the lungs is consequently increased. The action of the diaphragm cannot be seen very clearly but the result of its movement can be felt by placing the hand on the upper abdomen, slightly above the waist, and inhaling. You should be able to feel displacement of the abdominal muscles as the diaphragm contracts and lowers. Control of the breath stream for speech depends on the movement of the thoracic and diaphragmatic musculature, but we can consciously control the abdominal muscles more easily. The muscles of exhalation must be controlled firmly, steadily, and with no unnecessary tension. Any dysfunction of the respiratory tract will have a definite effect on speech. The students will then understand why opera singers do not eat heavily before a performance, and why a blow to the solar plexus is so devastating.

The Phonatory System

The larynx, also known as the voice box, is located between the root of the tongue and the trachea, or windpipe, at the upper front part of the neck, from which it projects. It consists of three single cartilages and three pairs of cartilages, and has a lining of mucous membrane. The primary function of the larynx is to act as a closure mechanism or valve in the respiratory tract to prevent foreign matter from entering the trachea (windpipe). As with other speech mechanisms, speech is a secondary function of the larynx.

The vocal bands are located within the complex of cartilages, muscles, and connective tissue known as the larynx. Energy provided by breath from the lungs activates these sound-producing vibrators. The vocal bands are relatively small in size, considering their constant use and function. The space between them is called the glottis. The laryngeal cartilages are moved by the contraction of the intrinsic laryngeal muscles resulting in medial approximation of the vocal folds, the closure of the vocal tract, and the blockage of air emitted from the lungs. The edges of the folds are forced apart when air pressure from below is sufficient, vibration of the edges of the bands begins, and fundamental tone is produced. The air escapes through the folds in a succession of rapid puffs during phonation.

The Resonating System

The fundamental tone produced by the vibration of the vocal bands is affected by alterations in the shape and size of the resonating cavities above the larynx. They are primarily the pharynx, the nasopharynx, and the mouth, although some voice specialists include the sinuses. It is the unique size and characteristics of the individual's resonators in addition to the quality of his laryngeal sound that enables us to recognize his voice from that of another individual. By changing the position of the

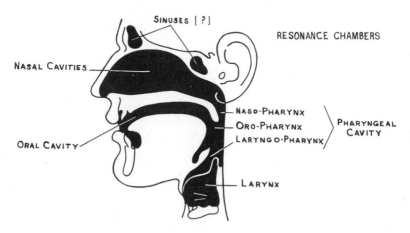

tongue and lips, the relative size of the pharynx and mouth are changed resulting in a modification of their resonating qualities. The resonators' prime function is to serve as air carriers into the body, the larynx, and the lungs. The oral cavity and the pharynx participate primarily in the acts of chewing and swallowing food. "In speech the resonators function in two important ways: the vowels are formed by adjustments . . . in the oral cavity and oropharynx, and voice quality is partly determined by the size, shapes, coupling and tensions in the resonance system." [3]

The Articulatory System

Articulation has been defined [4] as the production of speech sounds by alteration of the free flow of the expired airstream.

[3] Theodore D. Hanley and Wayne L. Thurman, *Developing Vocal Skills* (New York, Holt, Rinehart & Winston, 1963), p. 48.
[4] *Ibid.*, p. 48.

Although the primary importance of the articulators is in breathing and eating, their secondary functions make speech possible. While the vocal folds are not of themselves articulators, they have a small function in narrowing the glottis in the production of /h/. The breath stream passing through the narrowed glottis produces sufficient friction for the voiceless sound.

The soft palate, an extension of the hard palate, continues into the pharynx. It consists of muscle and other soft tissue and is covered with a mucous membrane. The lower free border of the soft palate is described as the velum. It can be stretched and moved upward and backward. This enables the opening of the pharynx and the nasal cavities to be extended or closed, which in turn controls or restricts nasal resonance.

The hard palate and the teeth are similar in that they are immobile parts of the oral cavity necessary for articulation. The lips and tongue act with them to control the correct amount of air needed for speech production.

The tongue, which is attached to the lower jaw, is the most "versatile articulator"; it can be "humped, curled, grooved and flattened." [5] Because of its mobility it is able to communicate easily with the other articulators — the hard palate, the teeth, and the gum ridge. The tongue, soft and pliable as it may seem, is for its size the most muscular part of your body. We distinguish five areas of the tongue useful in describing its function in articulation and in the shaping of vowels: *tip, blade, front, mid* and *back*. The *tip* is the firmed-up point. It articulates against the teeth in /θ, ð/, against the gum ridge in a great number of sounds and blends; it focuses the stream of air against the gum ridge as it curls back for /r/ and for the GA (General American) pronunciation of vowels followed by r. In other vowels it assumes its position of rest at the lower ridge and serves as a pivotal point. The *blade* is a broader area obtained by flattening out the tip. It is used correctly only in the dark pronunciation of /l/. The front of the tongue is the working part of

[5] *Ibid.*, p. 49.

175

the tongue in saying the front vowels. The tip must be down for the front to push against it. The *mid*-tongue is the rounded center used in shaping the mid-vowels, in the articulation of /j/ and in certain palatalized pronunciations like /hju/. The *back* of the tongue shapes the back vowels and articulates with the soft palate to form the consonants /k g ŋ/.

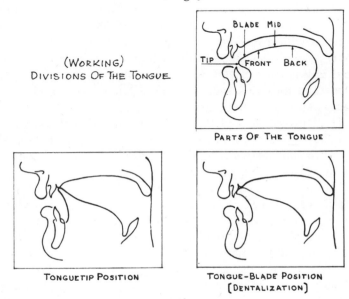

(WORKING)
DIVISIONS OF THE TONGUE

PARTS OF THE TONGUE

TONGUETIP POSITION

TONGUE-BLADE POSITION
[DENTALIZATION]

The mandible, or lower jaw, is another important articulator. The size and shape of the mouth are determined by the jaw, and it regulates the size and shape of the oral cavity by its downward movement. It also partly controls tongue position.

The lips, which easily adjust themselves in shape, are important in articulation. They provide the "last possible point of alteration of the breath stream as it leaves the oral cavity." [6] The lips stop or narrow the breath stream through contact with each other or with the upper teeth. They are therefore the active agents in the articulation of the lip plosive and labiodental con-

[6] *Ibid.*, p. 50.

sonants. They are also active in rounding the first five back vowels.

The above information represents the essential minimal background for a basic knowledge of the vocal mechanism. Further detailed information can be obtained in the recommended readings in the Selected Bibliography. We must remember that each part of the vocal mechanism operates not only individually, but is one segment in a unified system that permits the production of speech. All parts are dependent upon one another in order to accomplish the main function of the speech system — the production of clear, intelligible language.

Before leaving this area consider and discuss these questions with your students:

1. The organs we have been describing as speech organs have more essential and primitive functions. Can you identify them?

2. There is a direct passageway from the larynx upward and out through the nose. Can you trace it?

3. The tongue is moored to the floor of the mouth by a membranous fold called the frenum. Lift your tongue and look for the frenum in your mirror. Tongue-tie is a physical condition involving the frenum. Can you explain it? Why would it affect speech?

4. What is meant by the normal bite position?

5. What is a nasal sound? Can you name the three nasal sounds? What is nasality? Denasalization?

6. Yawning is nature's way to relax the mouth area. What parts are stretched in a yawn? Can you yawn at will?

7. Can you trace the formation of the following sounds: /m/ /l/ /f/ /i/ /u/ /n/?

8. Vocabulary checklist: palate, uvula, frenum, tongue-tip, tongue blade, front of tongue, mid-tongue, back of tongue, nasal sound, nasality, articulation, enunciation, larynx, vocal folds, resonance, vibrator, gum ridge.

177

XI

Reading as a Therapeutic Aid

———◆———

Oral reading, so important in the early grades, ceases to be taught or practiced to any great extent beyond the primary classes. All the while, the students' relationship to language grows more complex and demanding. In the primary grades, reading is largely a matter of recognizing words. After that, a second level, reading for ideas, is reached. Reading for ideas, in today's educational system, has been mainly silent reading. Thus it is that we find a great many students with a notable lack of sophistication in reading aloud. They lose thereby not only a power of self-expression and means for the enjoyment of literature, but also a valuable tool for self-improvement. This type of reading develops speech control while apparently providing enjoyment; it establishes good rhythmical patterns while it deals with thought; it increases self-confidence. We have already noted its use in the stutterers' clinic, and in the method called rate control. Reading aloud is equally valid as a therapeutic device in any clinic that subscribes to the point of view that a specialized corrective program must carry along with it the goal of improvement in communication.

At the secondary level clinics are often set up as half-major classes meeting five times a week. With most sound substitutions or dysfunctions under sufficient control for purposes of drill in the first month, drill procedures established, and remedial procedures for common errors introduced, hopefully we can assume that the clinician may have time to use the techniques of oral reading.

Not only will these techniques provide a means of general improvement in communication skills, but the readings can be selectively chosen to provide more natural exercises for particular sounds. In addition, such a discipline provides the clinician with a powerful motivation for improvement: the theory of compensation. We are forced to compensate in life for many things. The person with a foreign accent may have to read more slowly, more emphatically, in order to be understood; the lisper may rely on the purity and vigor of his vowel sounds to offset the remnant of sibilant cloudiness. Those of us with "trained ears" often hear public speakers, broadcasters, and even actors in whose speech we recognize the remnants of a lall or lisp. In the process of compensating, they have developed excellent speech.

There are students who develop into good readers, *i.e.*, good oral readers, without anyone's help, and are recognized and respected as such by the rest of the class and by their instructors. Jim or Mary, the feeling is, "have it made." What about Tom, Dick, or Harriet? The truth of the matter is that unless reading techniques are taught, individual reading evaluations made, and rewards offered for success in a graded series of oral achievements, the reading of the majority of our students will continue to be unimaginative, turbid, and lacking in communication.

Why, you may ask, is the teaching of good reading the obligation of the speech clinic? Is it not the duty of every teacher, the teacher of history as well as the speech clinician? In a limited sense, yes, but there are two very important limitations — time

179

and psychology. In a mathematics class, the student concentrates on problems. He is justified in thinking that when he has mastered them he has achieved the goal of the class. Similarly, in history he is concerned with a point of view, a body of fact. It is only when a teacher turns from the teaching of the course materials and states unequivocally that he plans to conduct a lesson in the techniques of oral reading will it become valid to evaluate the students on that basis. In other words, a student expects to be evaluated only for what he is studying. Only where the subject is not just "reading" but the techniques of oral reading will the student be prepared to receive evaluations that have meaning for him. It is with this point of view in mind that we include a short review of some techniques of oral reading.

LEARNING TO PHRASE

Focus the students' attention on the fact that the sentence is not inevitably the unit of thought, and that the reader may have occasion to pause within a sentence. All teachers recognize the fact, which Curry [1] has pointed out so well, that "continuity of words destroys continuity of thought." Although punctuation can be helpful, with the modern tendency to leave out commas where possible it is not a determining factor. It sometimes gets in the way — as in "Yes, sir," where the actual phrasing has fostered a new spelling, "Yessir." The following is one approach to the subject. Slanted lines denote pauses.

I go / but I shall return. (*Pause to establish contrast.*)
Whoever goes with me / will be rewarded. (*Pause to make a unit of the subject clause.*)
Going and coming / we lay waste our powers. (*Pause to separate introductory fragment from the main structure.*)
Gone are the days / when my heart was young and gay. (*To separate main structure from modifying clause.*)

[1] S. S. Curry, *Lessons in Vocal Expression* (Boston, The Expression Co., 1927).

My sister, / I'd like you to know, / goes to this school. (*Pauses to isolate parenthetical expression.*)

Many students today read on a "collision course." They speak that way too. A second unit that can be useful in combating this habit is the use of modern poetry, preferably poems that students will not associate with courses in English literature. Here is a challenging trio that concern school experiences:

ON THE WAY *

When he was four
the schoolhouse door
led into promised lands.
When he was old
enough to hold
books, not his mother's hands,
he ventured through
and found it true —
such worlds as he beheld there!
He took the path
to science, math,
and great words to be spelled there!
He never grew
so big he knew
it all, nor once pretended.
He had discerned
The more he learned,
The less the learning ended.

— EDSEL FORD

TO A PRECOCIOUS STUDENT †

Still wet with youth
You parrot answers
Borrowed from a book
And pass them out
In little gulps of truth.

* Reprinted by permission from *The Christian Science Monitor* © 1964
The Christian Science Publishing Society. All rights reserved.
† Reprinted from "High Points," publication of the New York City Board
of Education, by permission of Leo Kraftowitz.

SPEECH THERAPY

I like your spirit, but
You ought to dig down deeper
Toward the root,
And scrape the surface
Off the words, and calculate
What really is, and what's
Approximate.

I think you'll find
That wisdom doesn't work
Its way in haste
But often takes
The long way home.

It's when you taste
The bitterness in fruit
And learn that black
Is sometimes gray,
Half-truths are lies,
And fact is often mere
Misstatement in disguise,
That truth may leave
Its door ajar
So you can seek it out
With older eyes.
— LEO KRAFTOWITZ

HOMEWORK *

He bites his nails. He rifles through a book.
  His eyes are sad, as with some ancient woe.
And then a magic slips into his look,
  A spell of distant worlds and long ago.
  Forgotten, lost is all he does not know,
All he must learn. . . . The rambling of a brook
  Leaping with trout, moonlight on silent snow,
Exuberant grandstands, apple trees he shook
  Last summer for their glowing, spicy fruit —
These he remembers. These things are alive,
  Not like dull duty with its heavy boot

* Reprinted from "High Points," publication of the New York City Board of Education, by permission of Julian M. Drachman.

Trampling his spirit, not the buzzing hive
Of stinging musts, but the high, challenging spaces,
Bids to his pride, welcomes on friendly faces.
— JULIAN M. DRACHMAN

The eye, students begin to realize, must be an ally to thought, and both influence the voice. The reading does not come to a stop just because the line of poetry faces a space. The reader should not drown in the cadence; his purpose is to transmit thought.

A first unit in phrasing may be followed by others such as the reading of light, humorous, or nonsense verse, which offers a particular challenge in precise phrasing and its concomitant — the use of the pause. Students may be introduced to this form by means of short, varied excerpts from light verse — to be followed by readings of their own choice. Story fragments, descriptions, lead paragraphs from newspapers, even mathematical problems, provide exercise material in phrasing. When the students learn to phrase their reading, they will have taken the most important step possible in self-improvement in communication.

By and large, however, the teacher will avoid positive rules for phrasing, except, perhaps, for some suggestive ones such as:

- It is generally wrong to separate the object from its verb. (Herein, he may point out, lies the difference between the grammatical terms "predicate" and "predicate verb.")
- It is often possible to pause after the subject, very much like a speaker announcing what he is speaking about.

Students will come to realize that there may be several ways of reading the same thing — that one reader will pause in one place, another in a different one, depending on what meaning he ascribes to the selection. Not all meanings, of course, will be valid in a context, but the differences of opinion that arise about them will only show more clearly the dominant role of thought.

183

Short Phrasing

In contrast to the students who read without sufficient pause are some who pause automatically after every few words (called "typewriter attack"). Such students read like this:

I pledge / allegiance / to the flag / of the United States / of America / and to the / republic / for which / it stands. . . . OR,

If / these poems / are read / as a mere / stream of / words / there is no sign / or evidence / of any thinking / on the part of the reader.//

If this is merely a fault of reading, without intellectual or psychological roots, it will lend itself to a simple and satisfactory solution. The clinician will block out the student's present pattern, evaluate it with him, and work out improvements. The student, with the new pattern in hand, will read the selection over again. Practice on this one thing will soon result in the elimination of the fault and marked personal growth in speaking as well. The clinician will further direct him to challenging selections at his own level. Here are several favorites:

CLOWN *

Even before you flipped the ear
Of the puppy inside out, or swung
On the gate, or paused to engineer
A hasty whirlwind or to twang
The willow's mandolin, or made
Sport of the washing I had pinned
Out; I suspected your charade!
Enough of your buffoonery,
Wind.
— ELAINE V. EMANS

SUPERVISOR *

A Catbird oversees the plot
and gardener, eyeing what is what
and what is not:
despite his many daily sings,
his sleek and busy self he brings
to check on things;
an extra well-developed sense
of duty sits him on the fence
to peer, intense,
and supervise the ways of man
as only cat and Catbird can.

— MARGARET SINGLETON

SUMMER SUNDAY †

The Sunday boats tilt handsomely on the water's
thick summer blue, skittering over waves
that parallel themselves before and after.

Gleaming in true proportions, boats behave
with holiday exuberance: a wheel
spins playfully; a deck that water paves,

dips and then rises, then begins to keel,
but rights itself; in galleys, tea cups bounce
their plastic out of racks as owners kneel

to pick them up. As dainty sloops all flounce
between the yawls and ketches, schooners boast
their flying jibs, and racing outboards pounce

with claws of foam, touching the furthermost
bounds of this Sunday world, then as the chill
of evening falls, all up and down the coast

the tired boats follow lights home until
in every harbor all the sails are still.

— NORMA MCLAIN STOOP

INFLECTION

As teachers, we are aware of the variations in meaning our voice can give even to a simple sentence. Is Miguel going downtown with you tomorrow? can mean:

(Inflection on *is*):   I want to know!

("   on *Miguel*):   Who is going? Really Miguel?

("   on *going*):   Well, what is it, yes or no?

("   on *downtown*):   In that direction? I thought he was going the other way.

("   on *you*):   With you? I thought he was going with someone else, maybe with me.

("   on *tomorrow*):   Are you sure that is the day?

The movement of the voice (a glide on the vowel of the accented syllable) to make these variations is properly called inflection. It is also one of the forms of emphasis. Emphasis, however, employs several other techniques as well. The basic thing that inflection transmits from reader to listener is whether he has finished his thought or not. An upward inflection at a pause, either within the sentence or at the end of it, is indicative of the fact that the speaker is not finished. How true this is of form and movement in general! Youth, gaiety, vigor, and aliveness physically lift the torso and limbs in upward movements, particularly in dancing; age, sorrow, and tiredness sag at the mouth and the shoulders; the whole body slumps. We have all heard the person who unconsciously lets his voice drop at every pause, or subconsciously permits his inflection to reveal a pessimistic outlook. He is in dire need of help from the speech clinician.

Today, more than ever, we must pay attention not only to what people say, but to what they mean by the words. At the turn of a dial, important strangers enter our homes, speaking of things with which, one way or another, we come to identify ourselves — "This week in Vietnam has seen fewer fatalities." If this is the sum total of the speaker's thought, both "fewer" and "fatalities" are inflected and the voice drops. If, on the other hand, the speaker's thought is that fatalities are but an index of success, and that, on the whole, the week has been a poor one if we consider loss of property, prestige, and the possibilities of peace, then "fewer" will be brushed aside by the voice, and "fatalities" will have a lingering circumflex inflection. The voice will glide upward to indicate that there is more to the idea in the speaker's mind. The words form the thought, but the inflection shows the speaker's intention with them as well as his intended relation to the listeners. Time and again, students must be challenged to note and express logical relations in the words that they are reading. Teachers have received lasting appreciation from students whom they have coached intensively for a particular performance — valedictorians, entrants in a poetry contest, or the cast of a play — because these students realize that they have progressed beyond their amateur status.

Inflection Workouts

1. Read five headlines as if they were questions; read them as statements. Note the differences in inflections.

2. Choose a short, meaningful (to you) statement on education (love, hate, war, etc.) from literature or from a book of quotations and read it to convey the thought. Be sure you know the speaker's intention and attitude.

3. Read a sentence or two containing words in a series. Take sufficient care to have the listener consider each one.

4. Read a short dramatic dialogue between two persons of different temperaments (good-evil; sincere-insincere, etc.).

5. Discuss the inflection in the following colloquy from *Hamlet:*
   QUEEN: Hamlet, you have your father much offended.
   HAMLET: Madam, you have my father much offended.

Why is it important to know what has gone on in the play? What words would Hamlet give particular meaning to by inflection?

6. Prepare the following excerpt for reading, noting words and ideas that are contrasted:

RICH AND POOR

For indeed the fact is, that there are idle poor and idle rich; and there are busy poor and busy rich. Many a beggar is as lazy as if he had ten thousand a year; and many a man of large fortune is busier than his errand boy, and never would think of stopping in the street to play marbles. So that, in a large view, the distinction between workers and idlers, as between knaves and honest men, runs through the very heart and innermost economies of men of all rank and in all positions. There is a working class — strong and happy — among both rich and poor; there is an idle-class — weak, wicked, and miserable — among both rich and poor. And the worst of the misunderstandings arising between the two orders comes of the unlucky fact that the wise of one class habitually contemplate the foolish of the other. If the busy rich people watched and rebuked the idle rich people, all would be right; and if the busy poor people watched and rebuked the idle poor people, all would be right. But each class has a tendency to look for the faults of the other. A hard-working man of property is particularly offended by an idle beggar; and an orderly, but poor, workman is naturally intolerant of the licentious luxury of the rich. And what is severe judgment in the minds of the just men of either class, becomes fierce enmity in the unjust — but among the unjust only. None but the dissolute among the poor look upon the rich as their natural enemies, or desire to pillage their houses and divide their property. None but the dissolute among the rich speak in opprobrious terms of the vices and follies of the poor.

— JOHN RUSKIN: CROWN OF WILD OLIVES

PITCH AND INTONATION

Every language has its characteristic melody, corresponding roughly, to its national character. Otto Jespersen has characterized English intonation as "masculine." The intonation of American English differs somewhat from the British. It is simpler, and, if anything, more "masculine," picking and choosing what it considers important. German is more regular, rhythmical, mechanical, very much like a well-oiled piston. French, *"la langue de la politesse,"* is somewhat noncommittal, lifting the tail of its sentence so as to better plunge onward into the next. The student working to improve his speech through reading techniques should be proud of the striding line of his language and willing to work for the voice control (see the section on breath control in Chapter V) that spells that power. He will certainly not limit this control to reading, but reflect it in speaking as well.

SELECTIONS FOR PRACTICE

1. Lists of things loved are a challenge to the oral reader. For a follow-up, students may be asked to compose and read their own.

UNWRITTEN REGISTRY *

Each, for his own remembering, has a list
Of lovely things, and yours may be unlike
Mine as the day from night; a river kissed
By the sun is my own, a flaming spike
Of hollyhocks may be in yours, while snow,
Light-swirling but persistent, is as fair
To me as music. You have hours that glow
Jewel-like and exquisite, and I have rare
Mornings and afternoons and midnights, too.
You've loved a city you cannot forget,
And I a hill and wood in April; you
Bird song and voices I've not known. And yet
My list is strangely similar to yours:
Each warms the heart, and comforts, and endures.
— ELAINE V. EMANS

189

2. Students' involvement in what they are reading sparks the drive to communicate. Carl Sandburg's "Jazz Fantasia" is a great favorite. Here is a student's parody of it, written when he was a junior at St. Joseph High School, Chicago.

THE NIGHT BEFORE CHRISTMAS *

*Drift over snowdrifts, slide on that snowbank,
fly on that long cool team-drawn sleigh.
Go to it, O Santa!*

*Drive your reindeer on the tops of the sleepy
tin roofs, let the sleighbells ring,
and go jingle-jangle with the
slippery North Wind.*

*Drop like a feather down the chimney, drop
soft like you wanted nobody awake, rush
like a racing car slipping away from a
motorcycle cop, ho-h! you Santa, mix
together candy, dolls, trains, ties,
toy cars — make two puppies fight in the
toe of a stocking and scratch each
other's eyes in a clinch tumbling down
the hearth.*

*Can the wassail . . . Now a tired Santa pushes
up thin chimney with a ho-ho-ho-ee
. . . and the tired reindeer fly to the
high soft stars . . . and a red sleigh rides
on the humps of the low river hills . . .
Go to it, O Santa!*

— RICHARD BARA

3. The use of conversational tones, reflected in the rate and inflection, is contrasted with lines of description. That single distinction will, if made properly, give the students a great sense of reading well.

* Reprinted by permission of Mr. Richard J. Bara and the *Illinois English Bulletin.*

Assume it is morning.
You know what mornings are.
You have seen thousands of them:

They rise out of the East, huge as the universe
And stand in the sky till noon.

Oh, you've seen all kinds of them.

Some come up dirty-faced, as though they had
spent the night in the gutter between two stars:

Some bluster, brandishing big winds;

Some at dawn, are like a streak of blood across
where night met dawn;

Some are all innocence, surprised to be playing
morning to such a little earth.

You know what mornings are:
— NORMAN CORWIN *

4.

TIME-KEEPER †

She winds her clock, and noting
The hour, inspects the skies
Where all is running smoothly.
She would regard with shock
The thought that constellations
Weren't geared to set and rise
According to the dictates
Of her sacred clock.
— GEORGIE STARBUCK GALBRAITH

5. How many of our students have been in the position of the speaker of this poem?

AUTO WRECK *

Its quick soft silver bell beating, beating
And down the dark one ruby flare
Pulsing out red light like an artery,
The ambulance at top speed floating down
Past beacons and illuminated clocks
Wings in a heavy curve, dips down,
And brakes speed, entering the crowd.
The doors leap open, emptying light;
Stretchers are laid out, the mangled lifted
And stowed into the little hospital.
Then the bell, breaking the hush, tolls once
And the ambulance with its terrible cargo
Rocking, slightly rocking, moves away,
As the doors, an afterthought, are closed.

We are deranged, walking among the cops
Who sweep glass and are large and composed.
One is still making notes under the light.
One with a bucket douches ponds of blood
Into the street and gutter.
One hangs lanterns on the wrecks that cling,
Empty husks of locusts, to iron poles.

Our throats were tight as tourniquets,
Our feet were bound with splints, but now,
Like convalescents intimate and gauche,
We speak through sickly smiles and warn
With the stubborn saw of common sense,
The grim joke and banal resolution.
The traffic moves around with care,
But we remain, touching a wound
That opens to our richest horror.
Already old, the question Who shall die?
Becomes unspoken Who is innocent?
For death in war is done by hands;
Suicide has cause and stillbirth, logic;
And cancer, simple as a flower, blooms.
But this invites the occult mind,
Cancels our physics with a sneer,

And spatters all we know of denouement
Across the expedient and wicked stones.
— KARL SHAPIRO

6. For the student who "can't see poetry" try this prose from the sports column of Arthur Daley in *The New York Times*.

CROSSING OF THE BAR *

The telegraph keys clattered with jarring stridency. Few ever had heard telegraph keys in Madison Square Garden before. But this was not an ordinary occasion. A 17-year-old boy had cast such a spell over 15,000 persons that they were frozen into immobility and bewitched into silence.

John Thomas, a tall and willowy freshman at Boston University, was in the process of making sports history. The roars of the crowd faded. The hubbub of conversation dwindled. Then it seemed as if folks stopped breathing. And across the arena the telegraph keys in the press box cut through the hush.

They were clicking as Thomas rose to his feet in the infield. He inhaled deeply. He tucked in his shirt. He stared at the crosspiece of the high-jump bar, unawed by the fact that it rested 7 feet 1½ inches above the board floor. Then he began his diagonal approach from left to right, four short steps and four big ones. . . . That Thomas failed at 7 feet 1½ inches really was unimportant. The bigger moment by far was his hitting 7 and raking in the pot. The kid wore no elevator shoes as did the three Russians when they topped 7 feet. He wore the same type regulation shoes as did Charley Dumas of Southern California in his breaking of the 7-foot barrier outdoors. . . . Thomas poised on the runway and swooped in. His off-leg sent the bar spinning from its perch, dropping alongside the young jumper on his back on the red mat. He didn't change expression. In dead-pan fashion he walked slowly back to where Charley Stead, the Villanova jumper, and George Dennis, the Shanahan Catholic Club leaper, awaited him. The animated Stead was all gestures.

"When you took off, John," he said, jerking his body in

* © 1959 by The New York Times Company. Reprinted by permission.

demonstration, "you didn't give it enough snap. Look." He gave with the pantomime.

"That's it," agreed Dennis. "Make that leg do the work."

Thomas nodded appreciatively. He sat down on his red pullover and rested, hands clasped across upraised knees. He dropped his head and meditated. Finally his head snapped up boldly. He got to his feet and stared at the uprights with calculating eyes.

The kid didn't miss this time. Up he went in a twisting straddle of the bar. About two inches of light showed as he yanked his off-leg over. Down he crashed on the soft red padding. He held his breath, blinked and broke out into a seraphic smile before dancing to the infield to be mobbed by his fellow athletes. . . .

7. Conversation, particularly dialogue, with a suggestion of characterization, is a challenge for the more advanced reader.

WEATHERVANE DIALOGUE *

"To me it seems unethical,"
The sparrow sang, "the way you shift
With every wind. No breeze too small,
No gust too sudden, thunder squall
Too brief. One puff, you change your drift."

"Away," the weathervane began,
"You sparrows have no valid cause
To twit our kind. We furnish man
With true directions: sky we scan
For news, obeying latest laws."

"Evasive answer," chirped the bird.
"You circle round about the point:
The wind can speak no truth. I've heard
Wind's loud opinions. They're absurd,
Inconsequent and out of joint."

"Sparrow," the weathervane declared,

* Reprinted by permission from *The Christian Science Monitor* © 1964 The Christian Science Publishing Society. All rights reserved.

READING AS A THERAPEUTIC AID

"I specialize in fact alone.
I can encompass what is aired
In every quarter, never scared
To face the storm. My truth is known
Whichever way the wind is blown."

A wind arose. The sparrow flew.
The windvane signalled what it knew.

— VICTOR HOWES

Appendix A
Sample Selections for
Speech Surveys

(General Passages to Test Voice and Articulation)

————◆————

I. DIRECTIONS TO STUDENTS: Read the following at a normal rate, and loudly enough to be heard.

Welcome to _____ School! There are many differences between a senior and a junior high school which you will want to learn as soon as you can. Among these are the regulations governing absence.

Notes for absence, written by you or your parent, and signed by a parent or guardian are due on the day you return. If the absence is to be of long duration, as in the case of illness, it is often wise to telephone the school or write to your homeroom teacher to tell her so. This is an area in which a little thoughtfulness goes a long way.

If, on the other hand, you wish to leave school early to attend a clinic, or for an approved personal reason, it is necessary to get an out-of-the-building pass in advance from the Dean. This will be issued only if written evidence such as a note or a clinic appointment is shown at the time the request is made.

II. DIRECTIONS TO STUDENTS: Each student is to read one sentence unless directed otherwise.

    A. I wouldn't do what he said, not because I couldn't, but because I know I shouldn't.

    B. American history was easier for me than world history although I did well in geography.

    C. Listen carefully in class, take clear notes, prepare the homework for each day's lesson, are three pieces of good advice.

    D. "All is not pleasure that is called pleasure"; "Judge not that you be not judged," are two examples of emphasis by repetition.

    E. She sat on the edge of her seat eating her sandwich, and watching the home team even the score.

    F. "Sheep in the meadow, fish in the pond,
       Cash in the bank" . . . is the farmer's bond.

    G. She took secretarial studies and office practice to prepare for a career in the business world.

    H. The best biscuits, pies and cookies were awarded blue ribbons at the baking contest. Cakes were judged separately.

III. DIRECTIONS: Read the following at a normal rate, phrasing carefully.

    A. They lost their way, but walked on looking at the wonderful shop windows, the roaring elevated trains, and the huge skyscrapers. Hours afterward they found themselves on Fifth Avenue near Thirty-third Street, and then a miracle happened.

B. He had often heard of government officials whom no plea could soften, but this was the first time that he had actually encountered such a person, and the memory of that extraordinary occasion lingered long in his memory.

C. The glory of the nation from its first beginnings right through the length of its extraordinary achievements was voiced in the story, and the work had been so well done that the ideas of patriotism and loyalty that it strove to express gathered strength at every turn.

D. If you singled out words like *ring, sing, thing* and practiced them earnestly, you would at length learn to pronounce them easily and accurately, for the pronunciation does not offer any difficulties that a determined student cannot overcome.

E. The bringer of news or tidings of events in the medieval world, staff in hand, would soon gather a group of men and women about him in the courtyard or marketplace who were anxious to learn if his stories held any particular interest for them.

F. It was a three-days' journey to the scene of the battle wherein the destiny of the country had been decided. The guide pictured vividly the scene of the struggle when men, cannon, guns and armament of all description lay mangled in the very fields that now looked so peaceful.

G. The journalist suggested in the columns of *The New York Times* that in the present crisis over oil deliveries, the average man with a limited budget might find relief in converting to gas.

IV. DIRECTIONS: Read the following in conversational form.

Good morning, madam. What can I sell you today?

Do you sell steel scissors in this store?

Stainless steel? Yes, indeed.

Well, what is the price of such scissors?

Several prices. You see, we have two kinds, those manufactured by the firm of Zeno and Zumstag and those by Smith and Sellers.

Which kind is the best for sewing purposes?

The Smith and Sellers scissors.

What is the price of those?

A single pair of scissors costs 68 cents, but we can sell you a dozen for $6.66.

Thank you ever so much. One will be sufficient as I am not running a store.

Do you desire anything else? We sell the finest razors.

No, thank you, my husband goes to the barber's.

We also have scythes, lawn mowers, rakes, hoes and spades.

I have no use for any of those articles, so that will be all for today. Please send the scissors C.O.D.

I shall send them as soon as possible.

Good day.

Good day.

For easy reading:

THE DOVE AND THE ANT
(adapted from Aesop's Fable)

One hot summer day an ant who had been pushing and pulling, biting and chewing, stowing and storing, felt very thirsty. She went down to the stream to get a drink. Leaning over too far, she fell into the water and was pulled out into the current. She was unable to swim in the swirling river and barely kept her head above the water.

A dove, seeing her distress and feeling sorry for the poor

insect, picked a twig from a nearby tree and dropped it into the water, not far from where the ant was struggling. The ant crawled up onto the twig which was soon tossed out of the current and up against a ledge at the edge of the stream. It did not take her long to jump off. So it was that she escaped with her life.

Some time after, a man passing by saw the dove and raised his gun, intending to shoot her. Just as he took aim and was about to pull the trigger the ant rushed up his boot, jumped over the edge, and bit his leg so hard that he gave a sudden start. This caused him to miss his aim, and the dove, flying off, was saved.

So it is, my friend, that one good turn deserved another.

Appendix B
Cumulative Record Card,
Case History
and Appraisal Forms

———◆———

Most schools and speech centers evolve their own particular forms for screening and diagnostic evaluations. We refer those desiring an in-depth presentation of items to be considered in taking a case history to Johnson, Darley, and Spriesterbach, *Diagnostic Methods in Speech Pathology* (New York, Harper & Row, 1963), pp. 23–110.

The following case history forms are serviceable, brief forms that can be modified or expanded by the clinician for his own use.

CASE HISTORY FORM FOR USE WITH STUTTERERS (Simplified)

Date _____

Name _____ Sect. _____ Counselor _____
Address _____ Telephone _____ Age _____

Parents or Guardians _____
Siblings (Ages) _____
Incidence of stuttering in family _____
Domestic arrangements _____

APPENDIX B

Onset of stutter _____
Description of stutter _____
    occasion of greatest ease _____
    occasion of greatest pressure _____
School history _____
    subjects passed _____
    subjects failed _____
    IQ _____ Reading Grade _____
    activities _____
Physical history _____
    general health _____
    eating habits _____
    participation in sports _____
    rest and recreation _____
    childhood diseases _____
Vocational plans _____

SPEECH APPRAISAL FORM FOR USE WITH SURVEY

Name _____ Section _____ Date _____
                                              Counselor _____

VOICE
inaudible _____
nasal _____
denasalized _____
monotone _____
singsong _____
other _____

ARTICULATION
lisp _____
lall _____
sounds mispronounced _____
words mispronounced _____
general estimate diction _____
    "   "   reading _____
    "   "   communicative skill _____

STUTTER _____
CLEFT PALATE _____ HARELIP _____
HEARING
    estimate _____
    report _____

APPENDIX B

FOREIGN ACCENT

mother tongue _____

ability to read English _____

ability to speak English according to Scale: A B C D E

ASSIGNED TO: _____

Follow-up suggestions: _____

_____
Examiner

204

CUMULATIVE SPEECH CLINIC RECORD
BUREAU FOR SPEECH IMPROVEMENT
BOARD OF EDUCATION-CITY OF NEW YORK

SPEECH CLINIC RECORD
(CONFIDENTIAL)

LAST NAME (PRINT)	FIRST NAME	ADDRESS	BOROUGH	BIRTH PLACE	END DATE
FATHER'S NAME	MOTHER'S NAME	GUARDIAN	DATE OF BIRTH		

SCHOOL	OFF. CLASS	SP. CLASS ENTR DATE	SPEECH DEFECT*			NO WKS	POS. WK.	PROGRESS (√)*			RECOMMENDATIONS*			SPEECH TEACHER	END DATE
			CLASSIF.	TYPE	DEGREE			POOR	FAIR	GOOD	DISCHARGE	CONTINUE	FOLLOW UP		

SOUNDS MISPRONOUNCED	s = 4	REMARKS		TEACHER	DATE
CORRECTED (CHECK)	√				

REMARKS	TEACHER	DATE

DIRECTIONS FOR MAKING ENTRIES

*SPEECH DEFECT
CLASSIF.— STAM, SPASTIC, LISP, VOICE FOR AC, CL PAL, LALLING, HARD OF HEAR. (H. OF H.), CHOREATIC (CHOR.), MISC ARTIC (ART.)
TYPE.— LING. PROT (L.P.) LAT. EMISSION (L.E.) NASAL EMISSION (N.E.) HOARSE NASAL, HIGH PITCHED (H.P.) ETC. GERMAN, SPANISH. ETC.
DEGREE.— MINOR OR SERIOUS (SER.)

*PROGRESS AND RECOMMENDATIONS
PROGRESS.— (CHECK) POOR=30-60%. FAIR=65-75%. GOOD=90-100%
DISCHARGE.— IMPROVED (IMP.) CORRECTED (COR.) UNIMPROVED (UNIMP.)
CONTINUE.— SPECIFY TYPE OF CLINIC RECOMMENDED AND NO OF PER. PER WEEK E.G. LISP-L.E. 3
FOLLOW UP.— ENTER DATE (MONTH-YEAR) FOR RECOMMENDED CHECK UP.

(over)

APPENDIX B

CASE HISTORY ENTRIES*

CODE SYMBOLS		
T = TEACHER COMMENTS	TPC = TEACHER - PARENT CONFERENCE
PR = PARENTAL REPORT	TGC = TEACHER - GR. ADV. CONFERENCE
DR = PHYSICIAN'S REPORT	TSC = TEACHER - STUDENT CONFERENCE
GR = GRADE ADVISER'S REPORT	TAC = TEACHER - AGENCY CORRESPONDENCE

DATE	CODE SYM.	ENTRIES WITH TEACHER'S SIGNATURE	DATE	CODE SYM.	ENTRIES WITH TEACHER'S SIGNATURE

* NOTE: MAKE ENTRIES FOR ONE OR MORE OF THE FOLLOWING ITEMS ONLY IF SIGNIFICANT

DIRECTIONS FOR MAKING CASE HISTORY ENTRIES	
	HOME INFLUENCES: LANGUAGES SPOKEN, SPEECH DEFECTS IN FAMILY, HOME PROBLEMS, ETC.
	PERSONAL HISTORY: NUMBER OF BROTHERS AND SISTERS, AGE RELATIONSHIP ADJUSTMENTS TO HOME, SCHOOL, FRIENDS; HOBBIES, INTERESTS, HANDEDNESS, PERSONALITY TRAITS, ETC.
	HEALTH HISTORY: CHILDHOOD DISEASES, PRE-NATAL OR BIRTH CONDITIONS, WEIGHT - HEIGHT - AGE RELATIONSHIPS, OPERATIONS, MED. TREATMENT, CHRONIC CONDITIONS.
	SPEECH HISTORY: DATE OF ONSET OF SPEECH PROBLEM, SYMPTOMS, POSSIBLE CAUSATIVE FACTORS, FLUCTUATIONS.
	DIAGNOSIS: FINDINGS OF SPECIALISTS, ORGANIC DEVIATIONS, PHYSICAL AND NEUROLOGICAL SYMPTOMS, ETC.
	THERAPY: PERTINENT CLINICAL PROCEDURES AND THOSE OF SPECIALISTS, ORTHODONTIA, SURGERY, HEARING AID, ETC.
	TESTS DATA: NAMES OF TESTS, SCORES, AND DATES, I.Q., READING, COMPREHENSION, PHYSICAL, ETC.
	FOLLOW UP DATA: SIGNIFICANT FINDINGS IN CHECK-UPS AFTER DISCHARGE FROM CLINIC.

Appendix C
Plan for Remodeling
an Average Classroom for Use
as a Speech Clinic

———◆———

This is the era of automation. Computers selectively check units for millions of telephone subscribers, mechanical "brains" predict the outcome of elections, Telstar and teletape relay messages around the earth, weather is predicted by satellite, language laboratories have become basic to language learning, speech and hearing centers are models of efficiency and specialized equipment — but the average speech classroom in the public school is no more suited to its purpose than a medieval castle to central heating. This is unforgivable. A room suited to the purpose of speech instruction need not have expensive installations.

It must, however, have the following: access to a tape recorder and a record player; tapes and a modest record collection; a lectern, bulletin board, cabinets, and bookshelves. Let us state categorically that there is no justification for compromise in regard to these basic installations. In some schools, for instance, a tape recorder is available on request. This is an unsatisfactory arrangement, for if it must be sent for, or extricated from a closet and set up before the class meets, then put away before the end of the period or sent on to another classroom, its usefulness is seriously compromised. A recorder or player should be able to be rolled out, rolled back and locked. This is not to say that small drill booths are not more desirable, but our intention is to make suggestions easily adaptable in the average school.

The room should be uncluttered, functional. A small platform is desirable but not essential. In some measure the student should be able to obtain the sense of a listening audience, to be able to project his voice toward an audience. The use of a lectern is of great value, giving the student both a sense of focus and that small bolstering that the beginner so often needs. The room should be adaptable to the more intimate give and take of conversational exchanges, buzz sessions. If it is to be used also for drama or drama workshop classes, it should have, in addition, a makeup shelf, mirrors, and drawers. These are easily installed, even in the average classroom.

Let us take a look at an average classroom. It is about 25 by 25 feet with windows along one wall — two, if it is a corner room. It has a unit of student coat lockers along another wall and a blackboard in front. There is a book-and-paper closet and a spread of low, narrow shelves tucked in under the blackboard. The room seats thirty-five students.

In such a room the following could be done within most school budgets:

1. Eliminate the student lockers and install in their place a strip of mirror, a shelf (10 to 12 inches wide), and individual drawers under it. This would be useful both for drama and workshop classes and for some forms of speech drill.
2. Provide movable seats instead of immovable desks.
3. Build a double cabinet for the tape recorder and record player which could be mounted on stands fitted for tapes

and records (unless the school is able to provide desks with the recorder and player fitted into drawers).

4. Convert or adapt existing cabinets to house cumulative records, mimeographed material, and books.

5. Provide as large a bulletin board as possible; one outside the room can be used for material of general interest.

(Our recommendations are minimal. For more detailed specifications, the reader is referred to the article "Recommendations for Housing and Speech Services in the Schools," *ASHA, A Journal of the Speech and Hearing Association*, April, 1969, pp. 181–82.)

The work of the speech clinician in particular is not limited to the classroom. Somewhere in the speech compound there should be a room, carrel, office, or cubbyhole where he can listen to students sent for speech referrals, coach speakers and contestants, do follow-up work for clinics, interview parents or take case histories. Speech concepts are wide-ranging. The school that cooperates in setting up efficient workrooms will find itself repaid, not only in better instruction, but in the betterment of school morale.

Appendix D
Scale for Rating Pupils'
Ability to Speak English[*]

———◆———

A. Speaks English for his age level like a native — with no foreign accent.

B. Speaks English with a foreign accent, but otherwise approximates the fluency of a native speaker of like age level.

C. Can speak English well enough for most situations met by typical native pupils of like age, but still must make a conscious effort to avoid the language forms of his native tongue. Depends in part upon translation and therefore speaks hesitantly upon occasion.

D. Speaks English in more than a few stereotyped situations but speaks it haltingly at all times.

E. Speaks English only in those stereotyped situations for which he has learned a few useful words and expressions.

F. Speaks no English.

[*] From *Educating Students for Whom English Is a Second Language.* Board of Education, City of New York, 1965.

Appendix E
English as a Second Language:
Direct-Learning Experiences

A Tour Through the Kitchen or Home Economics Room

In learning a language, it is very useful to associate a word with its image. The school kitchen or home economics room provides many artifacts that the student may see at home and with whose use he is already familiar. Usually, such tours can be arranged at a time when the room is being used only minimally. The student may be equipped with a vocabulary list if the clinician chooses, and should be prepared to take simple notes. *Directions to students:* Write a paragraph or two describing the tour. Be prepared to read it to the class.

Suggested vocabulary:

employees	How many employees are there?
cook	Are you a cook? Why do you wear a cook's hat?
hot lunches	Do you serve hot lunches?

Suggested vocabulary:

cold food	May I buy cold food, too?
cafeteria	May I sit with my friends in the cafeteria?
tray	Where do I get a tray?
token	Who gives out lunch tokens?
knife, fork, spoon	How may I get a knife? fork? spoon?
wash the dishes	Does the automatic dishwater wash the dishes?
menu	Who makes up the menu?
equipment	What is the name of that? A *stove,* a gas *range,* an *oven,* the *refrigerator, sink.*
pantry	Food in cans or boxes is kept in a special room, the pantry.
dumbwaiter	Some food is sent upstairs in the dumbwaiter.
price	What is the price of the hot lunch?
sandwich	May I buy a sandwich in school?
orange drink	Do you have a fruit drink?

Buying an Automobile (for more advanced students)

Suggested vocabulary

steering wheel, fender, brake, headlights, parking lights, gas tank, oil filter, windshield, windshield wipers, horn, gears, automatic shift, speedometer, signal lights, bumpers, emergency brake, ignition, gas pedal, trunk

Conversation

CUSTOMER: We saw your advertisement. We would like to see the Dodge you have for sale.

SELLER: I would be happy to show it to you. You know it is a '64 convertible, and in very good condition. I always take care of my cars.

212

Conversation

CUSTOMER: Is it automatic or standard shift?

SELLER: It is fully automatic with power steering, but no power brakes.

CUSTOMER: I do not like power brakes. May we test-drive it?

SELLER: Certainly, here is the key. Shall I go with you?

CUSTOMER: Yes, please do. (They get in.) It drives very well, and has good power. Has it been inspected this year yet?

SELLER: Oh, yes. I had it inspected a month ago. The tires are not new, but they are in good condition. You should get plenty of mileage from them.

CUSTOMER: I like this car very much. How much are you asking for it?

SELLER: I am asking $350 for it. It is a bargain at the price.

CUSTOMER: Would it be satisfactory to you if I gave you $200 now and the rest in two weeks?

SELLER: It is customary to pay at once for a used car, but if you have references, I will be willing to wait.

Appendix F
Commonly Mispronounced Words:
Spelling Variants of
the Vowel Sounds

———◆———

eɪ   ail, freight, deign, matinee, melee, gaol, gauge, ay, alias, heinous, veil, gratis, status, apparatus, passé, attaché, Abel, Raymond

i   scheme, eyrie, era, quay, sardine, physique, suite, siesta, creek, sleek, clique, intrigue, vis-à-vis, Portuguese, subpoena, caprice, debris

aɪ   life, awry, slimy, horizon, Cairo, aisle, guile, sleight, geyser, grimy, bronchitis, ally, carbine, decisive, isolation, inquiry, appendicitis, sinecure, aye

ou   gross, chauvinist, vaudeville, bureau, bolt, revolt, chorus, brooch, below, abdomen, soviet, beau, encroach, Roosevelt, mediocre, yolk, Colgate

ju   produce, institute, tune, feud, neuter, nuisance, queue, constitution, avenue, student, duty, culinary, fusion, usual, knew, Butte, absolute

æ   camp, maladies, tassel, plaid, guimpe, bivouac, bade,

214

granary, harass, lasso, asphalt, aquatic, flag, attitude, larynx, adversary, guarantee, has, had

e tent, deaf, any, Thames, again, says, said, heifer, leopard, guest, epoch, get, essential, cleanly, engine, zealous, tepid, realm

ɒ dollar, honest, gondola, yacht, coddle, wan, mongrel, combat, jocund, pathos, consul, coffee, squash, squadron, lofty, melodic, incognito, positively, wallet

ʌ humble, suggest, supple, subtle, sloven, hovel, mongrel, covenant, pommel, nothing, become, robust, adult, just, doth, compass, tongue

ɪ rich, pretty, been, surfeit, counterfeit, juvenile, sieve, women, reptile, syrup, mischief, abyss, Italian, direct, finance, genuine, infamous

ɑ target, soprano, harvest, psalm, almond, khaki, mirage, Martha, hearth, guava, sergeant, qualm, hurrah, entente

a (optional variant) ask, after, dance, basket, chance, advance, askance, glance, romance, past, last, master, bask, Alaska, France, class, pass, glass, mast

ɛɚ dare, square, bear, parent, garish, affair, heiress, fairy, debonair, laird, compare, lair, mohair, blare, solitaire, wherefore

ɔ hall, pauper, laurel, faucet, because, palfrey, appall, lorgnette, corps, cornice, daughter, wrought, falter, exhaust, water, sought, awning, tornado

ɜ clerk, prefer, myrrh, myrmidon, circus, turmoil, adjourn, dearth, service, myrtle, hearse, curse, averse, colonel, squirrel, skirmish, demur

u moon, routine, bouquet, silhouette, druid, canoe, ruthless, ghoul, Sioux, scruple, rendezvous, lose, rheumatism, cruise, wound, boom, maneuver, prudent, roof

ʊ wood, pulpit, pull, book, wolf, bushel, soot, bullion,

ɔɪ bulletin, Worcester, sugar, cushion, put, would, butcher, woman, worsted, pulley, bosom, Pullman, rook, woolen

coil, loiter, moist, hoist, alloy, poignant, groin, boisterous, typhoid, adjoin, foist, cloister, doily, voyage, sirloin, viceroy, royal, poison, appoint, ointment

ɑʊ cloud, rout, howitzer, devour, council, crouch, sour, cowl, gout, owl, lowery, our, vouchsafe, chowder, rouse, bough, dowry, gown, drought, drowned, abound, viscount

ə umbrella, sarsaparilla, algebra, Cuba, soda, comma, Florida, America, idea, Ida, satyr, martyr

Appendix G
Practice Sheets for
Common Mispronunciations

———◆———

The Sound of /aɪ/

The mispronunciation of the sound /aɪ/ is called a vulgarism. Correctly pronounced, it consists of two front vowels; incorrectly pronounced, the first element drops to the back and is rounded. No speech pattern should be considered adequate in which this sound is pronounced incorrectly.

Practice phrases

arriving at Idlewild
by and by
a sty on my eye
tie your tie
flies high in the sky
she cried and sighed
I'd climb the highest mountain
silent night, holy night

sign of triumph
mighty chimes
he rides the bike
bright as a bride
liable to be filed
over the horizon I fly
signifying childhood
a kite out of sight

Practice phrases

diving for diamonds   rise and put the light on
ride the white horse   an idle tyrant

Practice sentences

1. Side by side they climbed the high mountain.
2. Ira and Irene tried to contact Myra and Michael.
3. Slices of pineapple pie were sold at five cents a slice.
4. The light from the pine logs in the fireplace burnt bright in the gathering twilight.
5. Kind words and bright smiles greeted the tired travelers.
6. The nine survivors of the plane crash testified at the trial.
7. The climate in Tucson is hot and dry in the months of June and July.
8. Driving from Elmira, he passed through Iowa and Ohio.
9. Ice cream and ices are delightful in the summertime.
10. Try with all your might to remain calm in troubled times.

Checklist of words: plight, sight, flight, bite, bright, might, right, tight, night, light, fright, plying, sighing, buying, highly, my, tie, nigh, lie, fight, fly, sign, find, mind, mine

The Sound of /æ/

The mispronunciation of the sound /æ/ is called a vulgarism. It should be avoided not only for that reason, but because the strain on the throat causes fatigue for both speaker and listener. Listen to the sound pronounced correctly, then pronounce it yourself, opening the mouth wider, pulling the corners back. The æ is the fifth sound down on the vowel scale.

Practice list

grab bag   the class cat   Aladdin's lamp
Mad Hatter   last Saturday   manual action
pass out of class   rapid action   cash balance
bad transaction   a laughing man   at random
handling the matter   stand fast   the Panhandle

218

Practice list

Akron	classified ad	rather than
Abilene	rat trap	Katherine Mansfield
allied ammunition	clad scantily	Miami
bad manners	Alan Ladd	San Francisco
masks and dances	Marlon Brando	California
hand me the candy	catch as catch can	taxicab
a Sad Sack in Bagdad	apples and cabbages	fantastically acrobatic
afternoon nap	Yankee valor	

Practice sentences

1. If a child with a bag of candy is as happy as a gamboling lamb, would a gamboling lamb with a bag of candy be as happy as a child?
2. "Handsome is as handsome does" is an old adage.
3. Jack, the captain of the track and basketball teams, ran to the line with the black banner. The announcer shouted for all athletes to toe the line. They wouldn't let him play, however, because he had a low average in Latin and Spanish.
4. Randy is not an acrobat but a student actor. As a matter of fact, he is the best actor in the dramatics class. He has an accurate vocabulary and a pleasing manner.
5. The Mad Hatter sat, and stormed
   At the rat, who dozed on without a care
   Of the Mad Hare's jabs and digging stabs,
   The rodent slept, unaware.
   "Alack! Alack! She'll never come back!"
   Sobbed the Hare with a sorrowful groan.
   When at last, to a slap, the rat woke from his nap
   And uttered a horrified moan.
   "Of what do you speak?
   Of whom do you shriek?
   And why so aghast do you stand?"

The Hare with a sigh his teardrops did dry,
"It's about Alice of Wonderland."
Now thoroughly startled from out of his nap,
The rat anxiously queried, "Did she have a mishap?"
"A mishap to us," cried the Hatter, "Alas!
Alice has gone back through the Looking Glass."

Appendix H
Checklist of Strong and
Weak Forms

———◆———

WORD	STRONG	WEAK
a	eɪ	ə
am	æm	əm, m
and	ænd	ənd, nd, ən, n
are	ɑ, ɑɹ	ə, ɚ
as	æz	əz
at	æt	ət
but	bʌt	bət
can (be able)	kæn	kən, kn
cannot	kænɒt	kæn'ət, kənɒt', kænt, kənt
could	kʊd	kəd

Checklist of Strong and Weak Forms

WORD	STRONG	WEAK
do	du	dʊ, də, d
does	dʌz	dəz, dz
for	fɔ, fɔʴ	fə, fəʴ
from	frɒm	frəm
had	hæd	həd, əd, d
has	hæz	həz, əz, z, s
have	hæv	həv, əv, v
he	hi	hɪ, i, ɪ
her	hɜ, hɝ	hə, həʴ, ɜ, ɝ, əʴ
his	hɪz	ɪz
must	mʌst	məst
not	nɒt	nət, nt
of	ɒv	əv, v
or	ɔ, ɔʴ	ə, əʴ
shall	ʃæl	ʃəl, ʃl
she	ʃi	ʃɪ
should	ʃʊd	ʃəd
some	sʌm	səm
than	ðæn	ðən, ðn
that	ðæt	ðət
the	ði	ðə, ðɪ
them	ðem	ðəm, ðm
there	ðɛə, ðɛɚ	ðə, ðɚ

Checklist of Strong and Weak Forms

WORD	STRONG	WEAK
to	tu	tʊ, tə
us	ʌs	əs
was	wɒz	wəz
will	wɪl	l
would	wʊd	wəd, əd, d

Selected Bibliography

ALLEN, HAROLD B., *Teaching English as a Second Language: A Book of Readings.* New York, McGraw-Hill, 1965.

ANDERSON, VIRGIL A., *Improving the Child's Speech.* New York, Oxford University Press, 1953.

—— *Training the Speaking Voice,* 2nd ed. New York, Oxford University Press, 1961.

BENDER, JAMES F., and KLEINFELD, VICTOR M., *Speech Correction Manual,* New York, Farrar & Rinehart, 1937.

BERRY, MILDRED F., and EISENSON, JON, *Speech Disorders.* New York, Appleton-Century-Crofts, 1956.

BLACK, MARTHA E., *Speech Correction in the Schools.* Englewood Cliffs, N.J., Prentice-Hall, 1964.

BRADEN, WALDO W., *Speech Methods and Resources.* New York, Harper & Row, 1961.

BRODNITZ, FRIEDRICH S., *Keep Your Voice Healthy.* New York, Harper & Row, 1953.

BRONSTEIN, ARTHUR, J., *The Pronunciation of American English.* New York, Appleton-Century-Crofts, 1960.

—— and JACOBY, BEATRICE, *Your Speech and Voice*. New York, Random House, 1967.

—— and OGILVIE, MARDEL, "A Report on Methods, Content and Speech Standards of the Oral Interview Used in Teachers' Qualifying Examinations," *Speech Bulletin* of the New York City Speech Association (March, 1951).

CURRY, S. S., *Lessons in Vocal Expression*. Boston, The Expression Co., 1927.

DIXSON, R. J., *Everyday Dialogues in English*. New York, Regents Publishing Co., 1953.

—— *Practical Guide to the Teaching of English as a Foreign Language*. New York, Regents Publishing Co., 1960.

EISENSON, JON, ed., *Stuttering: A Symposium*. New York, Harper & Row, 1958.

—— and OGILVIE, MARDEL, *Speech Correction in the Schools*. New York, Macmillan, 1957.

FAIRBANKS, GRANT, *Voice and Articulation Drillbook*, 2nd ed. New York, Harper & Row, 1960.

FINOCCHIARO, MARY, *Teaching English as a Second Language*. New York, Harper & Brothers, 1958.

FISHER, HILDA, *Improving Voice and Articulation*. Boston, Houghton Mifflin, 1966.

FROESCHELS, EMIL, *Twentieth Century Speech and Voice Correction*. New York, Macmillan, 1957.

GRAY, GILES, and WISE, CLAUDE M., *Bases of Speech*, 3rd ed. New York, Harper & Row, 1959.

GRIFFITH, FRANCIS, NELSON, CATHERINE, and STASHEFF, EDWARD, *Your Speech*. Harcourt, Brace & World, 1960.

HANLEY, T. D., and THURMAN, W. L., *Developing Vocal Skills*. New York, Holt, Rinehart & Winston, 1942.

HAHN, EUGENE, *Stuttering: Significant Theories and Therapies* (Prepared by Elise S. Hahn). Stanford, Stanford University Press, 1958.

HEINBERG, PAUL, *Voice Training for Speaking and Reading Aloud*. New York, Ronald, 1964.

HUCKLEBERRY, ALLAN W., and STROTHER, EDWARD S., *Speech Education for the Elementary Teacher.* Boston, Allyn & Bacon, 1966.

HURST, CHARLES G., JR., and JONES, WALLACE L., "Psychological Concomitants of Sub-Standard Speech," *The Journal of Negro Education* (Fall, 1966), pp. 409–419.

JACOBSEN, EDWARD, *Progressive Relaxation,* 2nd ed. Chicago, University of Chicago Press, 1951.

JESPERSEN, OTTO, *Growth and Structure of the English Language.* New York, Appleton-Century-Crofts, 1929.

JOHNSON, WENDELL, and OTHERS, *Speech-Handicapped School Children,* 3rd ed. New York, Harper & Row, 1967.

KAPLAN, HAROLD N., *Anatomy and Physiology of Speech.* New York, McGraw-Hill, 1960.

KENYON, J. S., *American Pronunciation,* 10th ed. Ann Arbor, Mich., George Wahr, 1958.

KLINGHARDT, HERMANN, *Übungen in Deutschem Tonfall. Für Lehrer und Studierende.* Leipzig, Verlag Von Quelle & Meyer, 1927.

KRAPP, G. P., *Pronunciation of Standard English in America.* New York, Oxford University Press, 1919.

LANCASTER, LOUISE, *Introducing English.* Boston, Houghton Mifflin, 1966.

MANSER, RUTH B., *Speech Improvement on the Contract Plan,* 3rd ed. Philadelphia, Chilton, 1965.

NEMOY, ELIZABETH M., and DAVIS, SERENA F., *The Correction of Defective Consonant Sounds.* Magnolia, Mass., The Expression Co., 1964.

OGILVIE, MARDEL, *Speech in the Elementary School.* New York, McGraw-Hill, 1954.

OLSEN, J., "Verbal Ability of the Culturally Different," *Educational Forum,* Vol. 29 (March, 1965), pp. 280–284.

PALMER, JOHN M., and LO RUSSO, DOMINIC A., *Anatomy for Speech and Hearing.* New York, Harper & Row, 1965.

"Resource Units for Classes with Puerto Rican Pupils." Resource

Unit Series, The Puerto Rican Study, New York City Board of Education (January, 1963).

RIPMAN, W. *Sounds of Spoken English.* London, John Dent, 1934.

SHEARER, WILLIAM M., *Illustrated Speech Anatomy.* Springfield, Ill., Thomas, 1963.

THOMAS, C. K., *An Introduction to the Phonetics of American English.* New York, Ronald Press, 1958.

Toward Better Speech. Curriculum Bulletin #5, New York City Board of Education, 1963.

TURNER, RICHARD, and FORLANO, GEORGE, *Effects of Basic English Instruction Presented on T.V. on the Language Fluency of Puerto Rican Children.* Research Report #1, New York City Board of Education (February, 1961).

VAN RIPER, CHARLES, *Speech Correction,* 4th ed. Englewood Cliffs, N.J., Prentice-Hall, 1963.

—— and BUTLER, KATHERINE G., *Speech in the Elementary Classroom.* New York, Harper & Row, 1955.

—— and IRWIN, JOHN, *Voice and Articulation.* Englewood Cliffs, N.J., Prentice-Hall, 1958.

WEISS, DESO A., and BEEBE, HELEN H., eds., *The Chewing Approach in Voice and Speech Therapy.* Basel and New York, S. Karger, 1959.

Index

INDEX

Eisenson, Jon, 76, 224, 225
Emans, Elaine V., quoted, 184, 189
emphasis, 186
  see also inflection
Engle, Paul, quoted, 73
exhalation, 172–173
  see also breathing
English as a second language, 148–167
  amount of foreign language mastery needed by clinician, 161
  drill, in clinics for nonspeakers of English, 149
  ear-training drills for common difficulties, 165–166
  nonspeakers of English, number in New York City, 148
  sample lessons for, 211–213
  scheduling nonspeakers of English for speech clinics, 150–151
  unique responsibility of speech clinic for, 148–149
  use of scale for rating pupil's ability to speak English, 149–150, 210
  see also foreign accent clinic; speech clinic for nonspeakers of English

Fairbanks, Grant, 14, 225
Farjeon, Eleanor, quoted, 71–72
Finocchiaro, Mary, 225
Fisher, Hilda, 225
Ford, Edsel, 181
foreign accent clinic, 163–167
  sample lesson, 165–166
  self-evaluation, 164
  use of vowel scale, consonant chart, 164–165
Forlano, George, 227
fricatives, defined, 129
Froeschels, Emil, 82, 225

Galbraith, Georgie Starbuck, quoted, 191
General American, vowel scale, 98
glides, defined, 129–130

glottis, 173, 175
glottal stop, 106, 138
Gray, Giles, 225
Griffith, Francis, 13, 42, 92, 225

Hahn, Eugene, 76, 225
Hanley, Theodore D., 174, 225
hard palate, 175
harsh voice, 59
hearing loss, 6–7, 59, 67
Heinberg, Paul, 225
Howes, Victor, quoted, 194–195
Huckleberry, Allan W., 226
Hurst, Charles G., Jr., 226

inaudibility, 66–67
infantilism in speech, 43, 52–53
inflection
  defined, 186
  exercises for, 187, 188
  in oral reading, 186–188
  upward vs. downward, 186
  vowel glides in, 186–187
inhalation, 71, 172
  see also breathing
Irwin, John, 227

Jacobson, Edward, 226
Jacoby, Beatrice, 225
Jespersen, Otto, 188, 226
Johnson, Wendell, 86, 95, 202, 226
Jones, Daniel, 14
Jones, Wallace L., 226

Kaplan, Harold, 226
Kenyon, J. S., 12, 226
Kleinfeld, Victor M., 224
Klinghardt, Hermann, 64, 226
Kraftowitz, Leo, quoted, 181–182
Krapp, G. P., 12, 226

lalling (mispronunciations of /l/, /r/), 43–57
  causes, 43–44
Lancaster, Louise, 226
larynx, 170, 173, 177
lateral, defined, 44, 129